A Gui

ZOOS

and

SPECIALIST

COLLECTIONS

John Nichol

CHRISTOPHER HELM
London

© 1989 John Nichol

Christopher Helm (Publishers) Ltd, Imperial House,
21–25 North Street, Bromley, Kent BR1 1SD

ISBN 0–7470–2410–3

A CIP catalogue record for this book
is available from the British Library

Typeset by Columns of Reading
Printed and bound in Great Britain by
Billing and Sons Ltd, Worcester

Contents

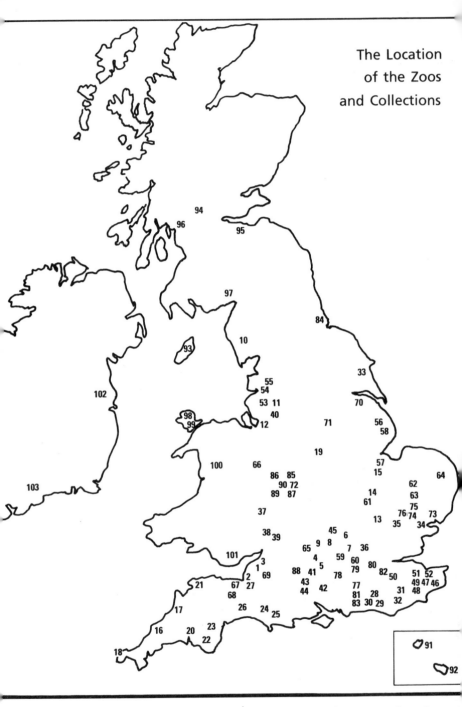

The Location
of the Zoos
and Collections

The numbers given on the map, to show the location of each
zoo or collection, correspond to the number given alongside
the name and address of each one in the text.

Introduction

This book is about collections of animals that are open to the public. Some of them are zoos as most people understand the term, some of them are bird gardens, some are city farms and some of them are wildlife reserves. There are others as well, but throughout the next couple of chapters I refer to all of them by the generic term *zoo*.

Most of the collections charge admission, but do read through the zoo pages carefully, because if you are fancying a visit to a collection and you are broke, some of them are free and others charge very small admission fees. All the city farms are free, and some of the collections run by local councils do not charge for admission either.

This book involved varying degrees of work by all sorts of people. At the publisher's office much time was spent folding questionnaires and stuffing them into envelopes, as well as on the phone talking to many of the collections listed in this book. Someone from every single collection took the trouble to fill in the questionnaires that we sent them, and a lot of care and enthusiasm clearly went into the bundles of literature that we received in return. Friends and colleagues visited collections for me, pretending to be the zoological equivalent of Michelin Guide inspectors. When I read through the reams of information I received I had to telephone many of the people who had filled in the forms to clarify certain points and to amplify others. Many of these conversations were a real pleasure. They gave me a chance to renew old, sometimes lost, friendships, and to make new ones. I spent a happy fifteen minutes one day talking about a whole group of fascinating fish that are known collectively as Rift Valley Cichlids. My informant worked at a collection where these animals are being bred in captivity and he was a most knowledgeable man. He was only one of many.

To all of them, to everyone who helped in any way at all, my thanks. This book would certainly not have happened without you. Obviously, for a book like this to work the information in it must be accurate and as up to date as possible, and of course I have tried to ensure that this is the case; but things change, writing can be misread or misunderstood, and errors can creep in very easily despite the fact that in the making of a book the text is checked again and again. So although I hope everything is right, neither I nor the publisher, nor anyone else connected with the book can accept any responsibility for any errors in it, or for any difficulties arising therefrom. If, when you read the book, you do spot a mistake, please tell us and it can be put right in future reprints. Similarly, if you visit an animal collection and feel there is something about it that should be included, tell us.

A Note About Animal Nomenclature

Where I have talked about a group of animals generally, I have used a small initial letter — e.g. deer — but where I have used a common name for a specific animal I have used capitals — e.g. Père David's Deer. In a few cases some people might argue with this because common names are often not very scientific. I have called all giraffes Giraffes because they are all one species, but I have no doubt that somebody is going to say that I should use a small initial since many giraffes are named according to the part of Africa they inhabit, or their patterns and colouring. So, for example, people talk of Vineleaf Giraffes and Baringo Giraffes and so on, but I feel one can take this to extreme lengths since probably every Giraffe from the most northerly in Africa to the most southerly has different markings, and one could end up with a hundred thousand different names. If you think that is ridiculous let me assure you that I have heard two academics arguing fiercely about whether a particular animal was of one variety or another. Since they are all the same, why not call them simply Giraffes. Goodness knows, there are enough difficulties in the world without inventing them.

The World of Zoos

Zoos have undergone a transformation for the better over the last ten years. Many years ago when as a boy I was taken to various zoos by my father, they were often miserable places. I didn't think that then, of course; I loved them and thought them exciting. One day I decided that I would become a keeper when I grew up. My father did not think much of that idea and insisted rather that I should become a fellow of the Zoological Society of London. Later on I did become a keeper for a couple of years, and discovered that the job was nothing like as glamorous as I had imagined. To a small child, however, a zoo was a fascinating place, even though most of them were relics of the Victorian era, still full of concrete cells and iron bars. There was even the odd bear pit in existence. Most zoos in those days kept everything from elephants to ants in the most appalling conditions, but of course little was then known about the science of maintaining exotic animals in captivity. Whereas some people regarded a zoo as somewhere to learn about animals, for most people they represented a fun day out for the family, and a chance to laugh at the monkeys and watch other people trying to look as though they were enjoying their rides on an elephant when in reality they were petrified.

I had forgotten, but now that I have started to think back, I can still recall the atmosphere of London Zoo 40 years ago. There was the bleak old Lion House with that marvellous furry smell inside that hit one as you entered, and those dreadful little cages in which were kept a variety of mice and other small rodents. Though the labels insisted there were animals in each of them, at the time I was convinced they were empty since most of the occupants were nocturnal and the streams of visitors peering through the bars never saw more than the odd twitch of a piece of hay inside the entrance hole of a sleeping box. And who, having seen him, can ever forget Guy the gorilla, that poor, mad, unhappy beast who sat for hour after hour in solitary confinement staring disdainfully over the heads of a generation brought up on tales of half-human apes beating chests and dragging off scantily dressed females to who knows what undisclosed fate. I remember too Bristol Zoo's gorilla, Albert.

Few people at the time considered such displays disgraceful, even though something didn't seem right about keeping such animals in this way.

Sometimes one forgets, or at any rate takes for granted, just how much progress has been made in animal husbandry. To be sure, there are still zoos that are a disgrace, though they are remarkably few, not that one would think so from the streams of protest from some quarters about zoos in general. Usually though, zoos have tried very hard to improve their buildings and facilities, and where there is a sub-standard display it is usually an odd one in an otherwise good collection, and as funds are made available such eyesores are disappearing. The recent Zoo Licensing Act should help us get rid of the numerous little cowboy operations that cropped up all over the country in the 1960s.

As we have acquired more information about animals and the way they live, we have begun to realise that zoological displays should change. It is no good keeping an elephant in a few square metres and hoping that the elephant and the public will find it enjoyable. Since the end of the Second World War, television has taught us much about the way animals live in the wild, and the advent of the cheap package holiday to exotic parts of the world has meant that many people for the first time have been able to watch animals in their natural environment. Both these influences led us to look at the same poor old elephant in a new light, and to complain about his treatment. Zoos soon began to respond to criticism, and the result was that the make-up of collections began to change. Although there are exceptions, nowadays small metropolitan zoos have abandoned the keeping of large mammals, which have appeared instead in enormous enclosures in our safari parks. This excellent start, and the new knowledge for the need for humanity and conservation in the keeping of animals, has led to collections becoming ever more specialised. Nowadays we find bird gardens, and butterfly parks, and aquaria, and reptile collections and so on. Even where a zoo keeps a range of animals in response to public demand, it usually specialises in a particular type of animal.

We like to think that safari parks and specialised collections are a new thing, but of course they are not. Long before the word zoo was invented, wealthy landowners were keeping deer parks and collections of waterfowl on their estates, and for centuries there have been aviaries at stately homes, or collections of monkeys or big cats in the oddest places, for example the Tower of London. The idea of zoos as we know them is, I suppose, a Victorian concept. They came into being at a time when the world began to shrink as more and more people started to make the Grand Tour, or to serve time in far distant parts of the empire in the armed forces, or as diplomats, or in commerce.

Early television programmes about animals proved popular, and a host of enterprising folk cashed in on this by opening tiny collections at seaside resorts and anywhere else that would guarantee a steady stream of visitors. Can you remember such places? They were awful, and mercifully almost none of them survived long, but at the time all one needed was a few rolls of wire netting, a pile of 'two by one' timber, a couple of hundred pounds for animals, and one was an instant zoo director.

At the time, any exotic animals that bred in captivity did so by accident. Frequently offspring arrived because the mother was pregnant when she was captured. The drain on stocks of wild animals was enormous, but air links with all parts of the world suddenly meant that animals could be replaced quickly and (before the fuel crisis in the 1970s pushed up the cost of air freight) cheaply. Some species were being exported in their hundreds of thousands every year. I well remember a bird dealer in Delhi offering special discounts for customers taking over 50,000 Tiger Finches each year. Nowadays things have changed. Many species breed in captivity, and zoos for the most part keep only those species that do. I was in the bird market in Delhi recently, and what had been a thriving community 15 years ago had now become a ramshackle collection of neglected stalls selling mostly domestic pigeons.

Many collections today consider it a matter of pride that almost all their stock is captive bred. Zoos throughout the world have exchange programmes and maintain stud books so that animals can be exchanged; and participating establishments can share the offspring of any resulting breeding. Quite a number of species of animals have been pulled back from the edge of extinction purely as a result of captive breeding programmes. In such cases, specimens have quite often been returned to their countries of origin. Sometimes this is not possible since habitats the world over are being destroyed, and the animals that once lived successfully in an area can no longer do so.

Another interesting change that has come about in zoos is in their staffs. There have always been strings of hopeful, intelligent and educated young people wanting to work in zoos. Thirty years ago they had little chance. Zoos made the point that a keeper needed to be fit and strong because much of the work was very demanding physically; and let's face it, if a prospective employee was not too bright that was regarded as a plus point since in between mucking out the elephants there was little to do until the zoo closed. Nowadays zoo staff are completely different. They still do the work of previous generations, but they have an interest in their work and a tremendous fund of knowledge. The Zoo Federation runs courses for keepers which can lead to promotion and therefore pay increases. Nowadays any zoo worth its salt encourages the keepers to be actively involved with the animals, and keepers in all zoos are fiercely protective towards the animals in their care, often regarding them almost as their own.

Another change that is coming about in the world of keeping staff is that nowadays a good zoo tends to let a keeper find what he is good at and what he enjoys doing, and then let him get on with it. This makes sense since, if a keeper is passionately interested in birds, he is going to make a far better bird keeper than a rhino keeper. Yet at one time some zoos ran a crazy system of changing their keepers from one section to another every couple of years, which made for unhappy and therefore inefficient staff. Another improvement is that nowadays women keepers are common whereas a couple of decades ago most zoos would not employ them except in the Children's Zoo.

Some people insist that it is wrong to keep animals in captivity. I cannot go along with that. By far the greatest part of our knowledge about animals has been gained by observations of captive animals. Of course, any captive animal must be treated properly, or there can be no doubt that it should be left where it is in the wild; but if an animal has all its requirements, both physical and psychological, provided, there can be no doubt at all that it is better off in captivity than in the wild. The thinking of people who consider captivity to be wrong is easy to understand — after all, when one sees a television picture of a beast standing majestic in an African dawn, it is difficult not to envy it — but what must be realised is that the animal cannot 'enjoy' freedom any more than you or I can in many aspects of our lives. It cannot go wherever it wishes throughout the huge continent of Africa; it is bound by the limits of its territory, and even if it wanted to move outside it would not survive if it did so.

Furthermore, even on home ground it is under all sorts of pressures, for not only does it have to find enough to eat every day of its life, and enough to drink even when all the sources of water have dried up, it must remain alert at all times so that it can avoid an attack by a predator, be that a lion or a man. Finally, all animals are under constant threat from an enormous variety of injuries, parasites and diseases, which is why one almost never sees an injured animal in the wild, for even mild injuries soon lead to death. This is fine as far as the survival of only the fastest, strongest and most alert animals is concerned, but it is not much consolation to the poor beast suffering pain and exhaustion, and a lingering death. Compared with such a life, a secure future in a good modern zoo would find rows of animals queuing up with their suitcases packed if they understood the choices.

So, for a whole variety of reasons, zoos nowadays are a completely different kettle of fish, and birds and reptiles, from what they were a generation ago; and if you have not been to one for a long time because you have believed all the anti-zoo rubbish that has been put about, choose one near you, and go and enjoy yourself without feeling guilty. If you do see something that should not be happening, complain about it to the person who runs the zoo, and don't be put off by any platitudes they might feed you. But do make sure of your facts first, for it is very easy for someone who does not understand animals to assume something is wrong when in fact no harm is being done at all.

I have heard many folk complain that many zoological collections these days are part of a big leisure complex. Zoos, they say, should be serious places where one can study animals in peace. I would be the first to agree that a zoo is not for light entertainment. I do not feel one should keep zoological collections so that everyone can go and have a laugh at the monkeys, but I do firmly believe that if any sort of education is made enjoyable, the information is more likely to be assimilated, so I do not find any conflict in having a zoo within the same grounds as Big Dippers and Bingo Halls. After all, if a whole family travels a long distance for a day out at a safari park there is no reason why each member should find lions as interesting as the next, and it is only right that each person should be equally able to enjoy his day out.

Pretty well all zoos have a job making ends meet, and it always seems scandalous to me that in Britain we have a national plant collection, or botanical zoo if you like, at Kew, but no similar zoological establishment. It is because of the shortage of cash that there are still some animal displays that have not been updated. As time goes on these are disappearing but there are still one or two around. The other thing that is happening is that in the light of increased knowledge it is now realised that there are some animals that do not do well in captivity, which is why it is unusual to find Polar Bears in captivity in this country. At one time most collections had one or two. Some years ago Zoo Check, the organisation that believes no animals should be kept in zoos, commissioned a survey into captive Polar Bears. The results showed that it is not a good idea to keep them, especially in the conditions in which many of them are housed. But what do you do with a Polar Bear if you have had it in captivity for twenty-odd years, ever since it was a cub? You certainly cannot return it to the wild for it would not survive. You cannot sell it or give it away because no-one wants it, and most people would object if you killed it simply because it was no longer required. All you can do is to keep it as humanely as you can until it dies, which is a very sad situation for the individual animal, but at least it does mean that Polar Bear exhibits are being phased out.

Most zoological collections in this country are run by people who understand animals and care about them, unlike the situation a generation ago when these places were being opened up everywhere simply for profit. Because they have this interest, zoo owners tend to have favourites, either because they are interested in doing some scientific work with a specific group of animals, or simply because they prefer parrots to sheep. The result is that many new collections specialising in a certain sort of animal have opened all over the country; and even where there is a large, existing collection, within the establishment there are nowadays groups of animals within the collection in which the zoo in question specialises. To take Twycross Zoo as an example: although a visitor can see elephants and lions and much else, the zoo is known for its splendid collection of primates. Therefore in this book, although you will find plenty of butterfly parks, bird gardens and the like, there are also zoos with general collections that specialise in one thing or another.

Since most zoos are teetering on the thin line between being in credit at he bank and going into the red, publicity is vitally important to them since most of their finance comes from gate receipts. Such publicity is usually in the form of stories about newly born cuddly animals. Just occasionally a bit of unsolicited publicity drops into a zoo's lap, which is exactly what happened some years ago at Jersey Zoo. Do you remember the story of Jambo the gorilla? Contrary to a still persistent myth, gorillas are nice guys, and the family at Jersey live in a super outdoor enclosure, when the weather is suitable, from which they can watch the ridiculous but entertaining antics of humans on the adjacent adventure playground. One summer's day they were all minding their business when a small boy fell over the surrounding wall and landed in a heap inside the enclosure, apparently unconscious. Jambo, the magnificent male, went over to investigate. He sat beside the child and gently felt him to see if there was any response. Nothing much happened except that the boy began to whimper as he recovered consciousness. Some of the other gorillas came over to investigate as well, and much was subsequently made in certain sections of the press that Jambo had chased them off and thereby saved the boy from further injury. In fact they, like him, were just curious, and he was only exercising his rights as the leader of the group. That is really where the story ended; keepers entered the enclosure and removed the child, who was taken to hospital.

The press, however, went wild, and headlines about 'Gentle Giants' abounded for days. Staff at Jersey were quoted as saying that they did not find Jambo's behaviour surprising, but that didn't make very good journalistic copy, and tales of the boy's miraculous escape filled the media's attention for days. It did Jersey's attendance figures no harm at all, and was a great bit of P.R. for gorillas the world over. I liked the way the zoo helped the story along by making sure the boy got a Get Well Card from Jambo while he was in hospital.

The attitude of zoos to the public is an interesting one that is rarely mentioned, unlike the public's attitudes to zoos. Most zoos are absolutely delighted to admit the public, not just because they pay for the place but also because many of the animals lead far more interesting lives than they would if no-one came to see them. The constant streams of passing visitors, and the strange things they do, stimulate the animals. In addition, good zoos see as part of their function a need to educate the public, and they respond to the curiosity of the visitors towards the animal world in every way they can. But the bane of every zoo keeper's life is the stupid behaviour of a minority of visitors. Virtually all zoos ask visitors not to feed the animals; nevertheless I can guarantee that on any visit to a zoo you will see someone sharing their ham sandwich with a deer or trying to persuade an Ostrich to eat a handful of pebbles. Not only that, some totally thoughtless people even drop litter inside the enclosures which animals can later eat, especially if it smells of food. Every zoo has experienced sick animals as a direct result of this sort of behaviour, and in many cases animals have died after eating something unsuitable.

I have heard parents in zoos tell their children not to feed the remains of their picnic to an animal as it might do it harm, but rather to pick a handful of grass and try that instead. It does not seem to occur to them that in order to keep the lawns attractive and free of weeds these areas might have been treated with chemicals to eliminate the weeds, or pesticides to get rid of unwanted parasites that might be harmful to animals. Such chemical cocktails are no good to animals, so please do not feed anything to them when you go to a zoo. Come to think of it, since you are reading this book you are not the sort of person who would do this kind of thing, but at least you can help to stop other people from behaving in this fashion.

Another really crazy thing that some visitors will do is to try to cross safety barriers that are there for their own protection. Parents will even sit children on the top of them. Such barriers are placed at a carefully calculated distance from the fence of an enclosure so that a visitor can stand as close as possible to an animal, but far enough away to protect him from possible harm. Cross that barrier and you could be in trouble. A monkey or an elephant or a big cat may look too big to get through the gaps in the mesh, but it is astonishing how tiny a hole is needed for a claw or a trunk or a hand to squeeze through — far faster than you can react. And what happens when a face is mauled or an ear torn off? There is immediate publicity and newspapers scream about lions maiming children for life. Only in the last couple of lines of column three does it say that the victim was the wrong side of the barrier — and that sort of information is not remembered. It is the headline that sticks in the reader's mind.

The third really silly thing that some visitors do is to frighten animals.

This is not usually intentional though there are people who happily bang on the sides of cages to get a reaction from animals. Usually what happens is that a whole crowd of children will spot something they desperately want to see, and go streaming across the grass towards an animal. Not surprisingly, the poor beast becomes terrified. In a zoo it is essential that animals are approached sensitively. I have heard complaints from visitors when they arrive at a zoo and they find that they are not allowed to take their pet dog with them. Most zoos will not admit dogs. Not only can dogs be a real menace in that they become excited and chase animals or bark at them, but they also urinate and defecate in the public areas of the zoo which is not pleasant and a source of potential danger to the stock. Canine faeces can cause parasitical conditions in other species of animal, including humans.

But provided that the visitors and the animals keep to their respective parts of the zoo and do not try to excite or harm each other, everyone can have a great day in a zoo. In the evening when the gates close a great peace comes over a zoo. Most of the inhabitants settle down with their evening meal. Keepers go round for a final check on their charges, and go home; and some animals leap over the enclosing fences for a wander round. I have seen this happen in more than one zoo, but they are always sure to return to the safety of their enclosures before the next lot of visitors pours through the gate.

Zoos are an excellent place for spotting animals other than those in the enclosures. Wild birds come to such places in huge numbers for the free food. Some animals are allowed to roam at liberty, and others manage to escape to take up residence in the grounds. I know one zoo where wild Edible Dormice have taken up residence, though no visitor ever sees them since they are extremely elusive animals and are in any case generally only seen when there are no visitors in the zoo.

If you are doing a project on animals, naturally you will research it in libraries and museums. But don't forget your local zoo. Any good zoo will be delighted to help, and nearly all of them have educational facilities. And if you are interested in working at a zoo, write and ask if they have any vacancies. Most people who apply to work for an animal collection do so because they want to work with the animals rather than because they want to sell ice cream or type letters. If that is your ambition you should realise that being a keeper is hard, cold, wet, and at times miserable work. Every day of the year, even on Christmas Day though the place might not be open to the public, the stock has to be fed and cared for. On a typical day a keeper will start off by cleaning the cages for which he is responsible, and feeding the animals. In the evening there is usually another feed. Most of the rest of the day is taken up with patrolling the grounds to keep an eye on the visitors and to answer any queries they may have. In between one has to collect or unload food from the stores, catch up an animal for treatment or because it is going to another establishment, do the necessary paperwork, pick up all the litter that has been dropped despite the rubbish bins that dot the grounds, and depending on the sort of place it is, gardening, preparing and mending cages, and any other odd jobs. Only very, very rarely is there the opportunity to take an animal to a television studio or to appear before a horde of press photographers with a cuddly baby. Zoo keeping can be very boring. After all, if the collection is kept properly, the stock should not need constant attention. Animals will usually get on best when they are left to themselves. I can tell you that there are few things more miserable than having to leave a warm, steamy mess room on a February morning to trudge out into a blizzard with a sack of grain over your shoulder, feeding the animals as you go and climbing over fence after fence in order to break the ice in the ponds. On days like that you never dry out, and at the end of the day you cannot wait to get your chapped hands and soggy feet home. On top of all that the job is not well paid.

On the other hand, when you have done your morning rounds, your charges are all well and the public start to come in on a warm summer day, perhaps especially to see one of your animals because it has made the headlines the day before, you don't feel like changing places with anyone in the world.

If you are ambitious, want to get on in the world and are keen to make a lot of money, then the job of a zoo keeper is not for you. Conversely, if material things don't mean much to you and you cannot imagine anything better than spending the rest of your life working with animals, then give it a try.

Many visitors to zoos fall in love with a particular species and feel they would like to keep them. Now I am all for people keeping animals, provided it is done properly and for the right reasons. I do not have any time for someone who keeps a single frog, or a bird to match the décor, or a snake to impress and frighten one's friends, but if animals are kept in breeding pairs or groups, and one spends time to find out about them, their lives and the environments from which they come, I think that is a good thing. Some animals that can be seen in a zoo are perfectly easy to keep provided you are willing to give them the time and care they need, and spend money on them. With regard to cost, calculate how much it costs to feed, house and keep the animal and add a hundred pounds on top of that. If you cannot afford that sum, do not keep the animal. You might be lucky and nothing untoward may happen. On the other hand you might find yourself lumbered with veterinary bills and new cages or repairs to existing ones, the cost of advertising to dispose of surplus stock, and all sorts of things. But assuming you can afford to keep an animal the first thing to do is to find out all you can about it. Read all the books you can find, not just a single one, and then join one of the specialist societies. There are societies for keepers of just about any animal you can think of. If you want to find out where they are the information is in my book *The Complete Guide to Pet Care*, published by Christopher Helm. This is the only place I know where you can find a list of nearly all the animal-keeping societies in Britain, together with quite a few in other parts of the world. The advantages of joining a club are many. There are the obvious ones, such as meeting other people with more experience of keeping the animals in which you are interested. There is also a bonus in that this is the best way of obtaining stock and equipment. If you buy an animal from a pet shop or an advertisement you have no way of knowing if it is healthy or anything about its history. Buy an animal from a fellow club member and it will probably have been bred in captivity and you can find out all about it. It will also be a fair bit cheaper than if you had got it from a shop. You will almost certainly soon find that your collection of one pair of animals grows and grows. Animals have a fascination that makes this inevitable.

Some of the collections you may visit encourage visitors to take up animal keeping, and sell stock. Some butterfly farms do this, and so do some aquaria. But do not assume you can keep any animal you may see in a zoo. A lion is not a good idea. Apart from housing, feeding and all other aspects of husbandry, you will need to buy an expensive Dangerous Wild Animals Licence from your local authority, who will want to inspect the enclosure and facilities for the lion before they grant one. Monkeys look most appealing, but do not think of keeping one.

They make terrible pets. They will probably not do well in captivity, and they will wreck the home in no time, not to mention your nerves. Monkeys do well in zoos where they can be kept properly in large enclosures, but they do need a lot of care and experience to keep.

Much of what I have said about monkeys applies to parrots as well. A small cage in a sitting room is not the place to keep a parrot, whatever anyone might say. They need large outdoor aviaries which are a long way from neighbours, for the din they make can be unbelievable. Other birds, however, can be kept at home, but you do need to know what you are doing, so the reading and other preliminary stages are vital. Birds have a high metabolic rate, and if things go wrong they can die very quickly. Some of them are pretty simple to look after, and if you are interested in keeping birds you should start with these. It is hopeless looking longingly at hummingbirds in a zoo and imagining you can rush out and buy a pair. They require a lot of experience.

One important consideration in the keeping of animals is the purchase price. One can buy a tropical fish of some species or a stick insect for a few pennies, but once you get beyond a few basic species, a hundred pounds is by no means excessive for an animal, and very many of them cost a thousand pounds or even more.

Which is why it might be best to enjoy seeing animals in a zoo. Some years ago a well-known actor was quoted as saying that zoos were wrong and that if someone wanted to see an elephant he should go to Africa, which is a great idea if you can afford it, but not everyone has the money to buy animals for themselves or to travel the world to watch them in the wild. That actor's quote sounded to me rather like Marie Antoinette's alleged 'Let them eat cake'.

Whenever I go to a new part of the country I always visit the zoo if I have the time, and it is interesting to compare them. What is even more interesting is to compare our zoos with those in other countries. Some European zoos, and many in North America, are splendid. None is perfect; there can never be a perfect zoo since we are learning all the time about animals' requirements, but nowadays in these countries most zoos try as hard as they can to get things right. Sometimes things do not work. The other day a friend was telling me that in one American zoo where the trees are artificial and made of concrete, the idea was not working too well, for when some of the monkeys tried swinging through them they were ending up impaled on the sharp ends of the artificial branches.

The further one travels from these countries, however, the more one realises how good our zoos are. In many places the zoos are so dreadful that one cannot ever imagine anyone keeping animals in this fashion, but of course they do not consider animals in the same way that we do. In many parts of the world animals are not considered to have feelings. They are either a resource to raise money, or a source of food. The problems that zoos face in these places are not those that zoo directors in Britain have to deal with each day. I was told by a director of a zoo in India that one of his greatest problems was how to prevent visitors stealing the animals' food from inside the cages. In the West one has to stop visitors stuffing it through the bars at the animals.

When one sees a tiger lying on a shelf just large enough to accommodate it, held in place by a row of bars in front of the animal so that it could neither stand up nor turn around, one begins to realise just how far animal husbandry has come in Britain. I have seen a tiger kept like this in a mobile zoo in the Third World, but I have also seen super animal collections. Nevertheless, it is usually in developed countries that one finds the best zoos. If ever you are in Singapore, go and visit the zoo, and also the Jurong Bird Park, both of which are good examples of what zoos can be.

So, during your holidays, go and visit some of the new generation of zoos, and learn to enjoy the animals. Don't forget that most zoos are also open during the winter, and although the weather might be horrible, there are no crowds and the whole atmosphere is far more relaxed. One can often see far more of the animals at this time of the year than in the summer when they become so used to seeing visitors that they often lose interest and wander off out of sight somewhere. Another advantage in visiting a zoo during the winter, if you are seriously interested in the animals, is that the keepers will often have more time to talk to you — unless you leave your visit till February, when any keeper will be huddled somewhere warm, if he has any sense, and you will not be able to find him.

How This Book Works

When this book was decided upon, we designed a questionnaire and sent it to every collection of animals that we could trace in Britain. You may be surprised to learn that there are over two hundred, and tracing them was not a simple task. Initially I went through all the books I could find about British collections and though this revealed quite a few, it soon became apparent that many have ceased to be over the last twenty years. I then asked friends with animal collections for addresses of others, and friends who are interested in animals for details of their favourite collections. I hunted through every single holiday brochure in libraries, talked to researchers on holiday programmes on television, wrote to professional bodies and bought newspapers from towns all over the country. We sent off the questionnaires and waited. Within a few days half a dozen or so had been returned, and that was that. A while later we sent out reminders and this time the replies began to flood in. In the end we received questionnaires back from about half the collections in the country. Since here was an opportunity for free publicity it seemed odd that all of them did not respond, but in due course some of the reasons why they did not, became clear. Some thought that each entry had to be paid for. That was not the case though we did give zoos the opportunity to buy advertising space if they wished. Some of the collections are small and run on tiny budgets which does not allow them to buy advertising. Other small collections already have as many visitors as they can handle and became frightened at the thought of a flood.

One day I was talking to Ralph Fitchett, who runs the Tropical Butterfly Garden in Cleethorpes, and he suggested that the reason more of the specialised collections had not responded was because some places, such as butterfly parks, do not consider themselves to be a zoo, and saw no place for themselves in a publication of this nature. But the word zoo is short for Zoological Gardens or Zoological Collection, and zoology is the study of animals. Since butterflies and parrots as well as elephants and people are all animals I would have thought such places are certainly zoos. One zoo I telephoned, said, 'Oh we get things like this all the time; we just throw them away.' This to me seems a ridiculous attitude. A few zoos did not respond simply because of inertia, and at least one lost the questionnaire somewhere in its top-heavy bureaucratic system.

A book like this only works if everyone else helps, so if you know of a collection that is not included, or have any comments on any of them, do let us know. And if you work for a zoo, try to persuade whoever is responsible to write in as well, and when the book is reprinted it can become more comprehensive. As it is, this is the only book available which presents the reader with information on animal collections throughout the British Isles.

When we received the completed questionnaires we also received additional information from most of the collections, so that either I or one of my researchers went to visit as many of the establishments as we could. This is not to say that we visited all of them. There was no budget for such visits so they had to be fitted in whenever someone was in an appropriate area, and had the time. Whenever we did go anywhere we did so as normal visitors. The reports on each zoo are the results of the information contained in the questionnaires together with that gleaned from the additional material that was sent in, and from personal visits. Where someone sent in only a questionnaire, not amplified in any way, information on that particular collection may be somewhat sparse. I telephoned many of the zoos after receiving their paperwork to find out more about them or to clarify the information contained therein. Only when all this had been done did I write the zoo pages of this book.

I must make clear that where I have made comments on any collection, these are my own. This does not mean that another collection is any less attractive or comprehensive or interesting. It simply means that I know a particular collection and I like it and think it is worth visiting. Equally, if I omit something about a collection that you know, that does not imply any sort of criticism, nor does it mean that it is any less good than anywhere else. Another point I should make is that if I have left out some points of interest from some of the descriptions, that is only a matter of space. I simply could not include everything, and some of the zoos sent in lots of stuff that I would have loved to have used. Where a zoo is incorporated with other, non-zoological features such as a stately home that is open to the public, I have concentrated on the animals and sometimes only referred in passing to whatever else is to be seen, even where the person filling in the questionnaire feels the emphasis should be the other way round, because this book is about animals, not about stately homes or museums or gardens.

Virtually all the collections stock animals other than those in which they specialise. Butterfly farms, for example, all have birds in their walk-through jungles. Some of these birds are there to control insect pests. One cannot spray a butterfly jungle with insecticide or you will kill all your stock, but if spiders are in the place they will spin webs that will kill off your butterflies, so a few spider-eating Chinese Painted Quail on the floor settle the difficulty easily and attractively. Similarly, many bird gardens have exhibits of chipmunks or other mammals, and the Falconry Centre in Newent has parrots as well as birds of prey. Unless these additional animals play an appreciable part in a collection, I have ignored them. Just remember when you go to see any collection, that you will almost certainly see animals other than those you expect to see.

If a person completing a questionnaire has said that there are no catering facilities or no restrictions, I have put the word *None*. If they have left it blank and I have not been able to find out, I have written *No information*.

I was delighted to discover how many of the collections actually have facilities for disabled visitors. You will see that very few do not. On the other hand, many are remarkably casual about encouraging children, which is a great shame since it is they who are going to be the conservationists of the future. I know there are some unpleasant children just as there are some unpleasant adults, but most of them are incredibly interested in animals. I would make a plea to more zoos to do more for children. There can be few countries in the world where public places are so reluctant to see children, but Britain is a strange place when it comes to attitudes to our children. If you are picking out a zoo to go to, and you have children with you, look through the FACILITIES FOR CHILDREN bit because a few of the collections are really great when it comes to young visitors.

When the questionnaire arrived at the point when information regarding admission was requested, all sorts of problems arose. Some establishments quite happily gave a figure for future years, while others made the point that they could only give figures for 1988 or 1989. Some zoos would not even make any sort of a guess at admission fees for next season. Whatever they said, I have indicated in the text.

We asked all zoos whether they had any restrictions and discovered that virtually all of them banned dogs, or for that matter, any pets. Again, almost all of them forbid the feeding of any animals by visitors. There is an excellent reason for this: all the animals in a zoo are fed a complete diet, and anything else, even proper food, upsets that diet and can cause illness and and ultimately death. It is not being kind to feed an animal in a zoo because you think it looks hungry. Zoo animals should all be given Equity cards for they are all brilliant actors, and their performances would often make a tax man weep. The only exceptions to the No Feeding rule are to be found in a very few places where one can buy special bags of animal food within the zoo itself for feeding to specific animals. Quite a few zoos refuse to admit unaccompanied children, which I can understand, but which I think is sad. One place says they only admit nice, cheerful people!

We asked each place about educational facilities. Only one or two had nothing at all. Most could supply information leaflets, guided tours, an information officer of one sort or another, and in most cases an education room of some sort. Many zoos could offer much, much more, and the greatest range of sample material such as is supplied to teachers was that sent to me by Cricket St Thomas Wildlife Park. Some places go out of their way to be as helpful as possible. Some of the Wildfowl Trust reserves do all sorts of things.

When we requested information about facilities for the disabled, I was pleased to see that most places had some sort of facilities, and some went a great deal further than others. The Wildfowl Trust at Slimbridge has audio cassettes and players that can be borrowed by the blind, and notices in Braille.

One thing I did not ask, and about which information did not always emerge, was about whether many of the exhibits are under cover. This can be important because there is nothing worse than going for a day out and having to trudge around in the rain. I shall certainly include a question on this next time.

When I requested information on the location of each place, it was always worded with the motorist in mind. That was my fault because that was how the relevant question was worded. When I looked at the promotional leaflets that most zoos sent me I discovered that a lot of them contained instructions on how to find the place using public transport. I think it is a great shame that everyone uses cars to go everywhere. Think what a much nicer place Britain would be if everyone left their cars at home unless it was essential, and I mean really essential. There would not be all those queues on the roads each Bank Holiday for a start, and after all there are not many places that cannot be reached easily by public transport. In many cases such journeys are faster and cheaper like this. Anyhow, I did not use the information about public transport because not enough zoos sent the information to enable me to standardise the layout of the pages, but next time I will. The only trouble with putting the information in a leaflet is that very often one does not pick up one of them until one is actually in the zoo.

There is, I think, only one collection that appears to have no interest at all in either education or conservation. When I asked about the latter, most responded enthusiastically, and some collections listed dozens and dozens of useful breeding results. Where this happened I selected a few species to give the reader an idea of what is going on. What you should realise is that most collections breed much more than is listed here or in their guide books, but of species that breed so readily, no-one bothers to list them in public, though records are kept internally. Some animals such as Indian Peafowl, Red Jungle Fowl, deer of various species, Bennett's Wallabies, Zebra Finches, Common Stick Insects and lions breed prolifically. One collection, when asked about conservation, candidly replied that nothing rare had been induced to breed, but common species were embarrassingly fertile.

Many collections are taking part in international conservation campaigns. Studbooks are kept of endangered animals in captivity, which enables collections which have specimens to exchange them to obtain the best breeding results. Most such deals do not make the headlines except in the case of Giant Pandas, which seem to spend their time jetting about the world to meet potential sexual partners. The captive breeding of pandas is not too successful as yet, but many endangered species do well in captivity, and numbers of these are returned to the wild.

Sadly, in many places from which they come, their habitats are being destroyed so fast that animals will not be able to survive long in them. Contrary to what many people think, it is not trapping or hunting that usually wipes out an animal, but the destruction of its home. When this is the situation, then of course animals are not sent back, but stocks can be maintained in captivity. Sometimes conservationists jump up and down in delight when they hear that some country on the other side of the world has brought in legislation to protect a species or an environment. Such jubilation is often premature since only rarely does such legislation prove effective. It is almost never enforced. Often today the only way of saving a species is to breed it in captivity.

One of the questions I asked was about non-zoological attractions. By far the greatest number of zoological collections in the country are next to or part of a whole range of other attractions. These range from museums and stately homes to funfairs, steam railways, motor museums and garden centres. Banham Zoo in Norfolk advertises weekend car-boot sales as an inducement to go, and Birdworld at Farnham also has Underwater World alongside. What is not clear from the zoo pages is that very many zoological collections incorporate the most lovely gardens into the scheme of things. Chester Zoo's gardens are super, London Zoo has lovely summer bedding schemes, Jersey is the most attractive setting I know for a zoo, and John Aspinall's collections in Kent, Howlett's Zoo and Port Lympne Zoo, have gardens you should not miss if you like plants. Those collections that have tropical houses are worth visiting if you like house plants, for they grow here as they are meant to instead of struggling to survive tobacco smoke and beer poured into the soil every evening. But please, when you go to one of these places, don't steal cuttings. I know it is tempting, but it really is not fair. If you see a plant that you covet greatly, ask at the office if they can let you have a seedling. If they have one they will often be happy to help you, and if they haven't they can usually tell you where the original came from so that you can send off for a specimen for yourself.

If you are thinking of planning a visit to some sort of zoological collection, but feel that you cannot look another Llama in the face, you should study the zoo pages of this book. There are some collections that are often overlooked. Have you ever heard of the Ferne Animal Sanctuary? It is a fascinating little collection of animals with no home, and if that sounds like endless rows of mangy dogs don't you believe it: there are all sorts of animals here. It has an interesting history too. City farms are another source of delight that are far too often overlooked. Even today there are children in cities who think that milk comes from Tesco, and that eggs somehow arrive in the house in boxes of twelve. As a child in London I recall a friend refusing to eat eggs because he knew they came from the back end of a hen, and could not quite make a distinction in his mind between eggs and faeces. And although I knew that the two were nothing at all to do with each other, and I happily ate eggs, eggs came into that shadowy world of reproduction which was never explained fully, so I was unable to put him right.

Townspeople have all sorts of confused ideas about farms and a visit to a city farm is an enjoyable day out, though you should not expect a smart, ultra clean environment such as is to be found in most zoos. City farms are often extremely scruffy. They exist on minuscule budgets which do not allow for expensive repairs to pens and cages. There are all sorts of animals to be seen at a city farm, however, and there is an added bonus that one can often buy produce from them. Vegetables that have been grown without all sorts of chemicals being thrown at them to help them grow to beautiful, tasteless rubbish which will comply with EEC standards. Even when one sees organically grown vegetables in a shop, one cannot help but wonder how much the truth has been bent. At a city farm one can see how the things are grown. There are also goodies to be had like goats' milk and yoghurt which has far more flavour than the milk you find on your doorstep or on the supermarket shelf. I would be the first person to admit that a large adult billy goat stinks like nothing else on earth, and after you have been handling one it takes days to get rid of the pong, but goats' milk is not like that whatever horror stories you have heard.

One thing that many of the zoos say in their educational literature is that so many visitors arrive with preconceived ideas about animals, ideas which are wrong, but which during the course of a visit they do not alter simply because they do not take the trouble to look at the exhibits. Visitors will arrive and make straight for the Chimpanzee enclosure. Frequently, even before they see any animals they will be making noises of appreciation, and while they watch the apes they will *ooh!* and *aah!* and laugh appreciatively. They spend some time at this. When later they arrive at a tank containing a snake or a spider, they will approach with disgust, make a noise of repulsion, and within seconds pass on to the next exhibit. Yet the snake is no more horrible, nor less interesting than the chimp, but people do not care to find this out. Most adult snakes can do you far less harm than an adult chimp could if it set its mind to it, and when all is said, the two animals are much the same. They each have brains and lungs and hearts and all the rest of it, just as the visitor watching them. Much the same happens when a Vietnamese Pot Bellied Pig is spotted. Isn't it ugly, they say. But what do they mean by ugly? I cannot see that the pig is any more ugly than a Pekinese, an animal that many dote upon. All animals, unless we have interfered with them, have developed to be as efficient as possible for their way of life in their special environment, and I cannot see that a crocodile is any more ugly than a Cheetah. This sort of thinking seems particularly silly when one examines the periodical surveys into what the public regard as the most popular or attractive animals, and the least attractive. Many of the results are predictable. Furry mammals with a short face and large eyes come fairly high in the popularity stakes, while the 'creepy crawlies' of the world are said to be the most hated. But then some animals appear on both lists. So, passing on what the zoos say, look closely at snakes and Wart Hogs and you will find they are every bit as interesting, and as beautiful as a lion cub.

The other point that zoos make in their literature is that the zoo is the home of the animals that live there. Please remember that and behave towards them as you would like people to behave towards you in your home:

- Do not rush about or make a lot of noise; walk quietly.
- Do not feed the animals, nor offer them anything to play with.
- Do not bang the glass or wire front of an enclosure.
- Do not leave litter lying around. Not only is it unsightly, but it can be dangerous for humans and animals in the collection, and expensive since someone has to be employed to go round and pick it up. That person's wages are added to the fee you pay to come in.
- Do not lean over or cross any barriers, and keep your hands well away from cages.
- Do not walk on gardens or damage plants.
- Do not chase or disturb any animals you may come across in the zoo.
- Do not play with balls or frisbees or boomerangs within the zoo.
- Do not play radios or personal stereos in the zoo.

If you think that some of these are obvious, every one of them is abused each week in most zoos. All these regulations do make the visit sound as appealing as one to a prison camp, but when you think about it they are all common-sense points.

At one point in my questionnaire I asked zoos if there were any additional costs once a visitor has got into a zoo, because there is nothing more annoying, when one has budgeted for a family day out than to find one is having to fork out for car parking, a visit to the aquarium, a fee to enter the nocturnal house and so on. The information that was provided can be found on the zoo pages. What it boils down to is that nearly everywhere the entrance fee covers all the parking and entrance to all zoological exhibitions, though things like train rides and amusements and so on are almost always extra. It should be noted that what the entrance fee never does cover is anything the visitor may choose to eat or drink, and what he may want to buy from the gift shop in the way of souvenirs. I think every single establishment listed in this book has a shop where you can buy something. If you are a photographer you should be aware that most zoo shops sell film stock for most cameras, but usually only for colour prints.

Food in zoo outlets can be anything from absolutely awful to well worth eating. If you do find yourself faced with a dreadful meal, tell the manager that you are not satisfied, and tell the zoo as well. Only if they receive a constant string of complaints will the service change for the better. And while we are on the subject of catering, it ought to be noted that in some zoos many of the catering facilities close down in the winter. Where this is so, it is indicated in the information given in zoo pages.

Most of the bigger zoos are open every day of the year apart from Christmas Day, but some smaller places open only during the summer. This information is also given. One or two places, however, have such very strange opening dates and times that you should make sure you have understood them before you make a long journey, and if you are in any doubt, telephone. One of the Wildfowl Trust reserves is open only in the winter. As I said somewhere else, most zoos are very happy to welcome visitors, but reading through the questionnaires one gets the impression that one or two of the smaller, private collections really resent them, and only grudgingly let them in to pay for the food. This does seem a great shame.

Many of these establishments have all sorts of facilities for teachers. Phone and ask about them: you will often be surprised at what is available. Many places will be happy for a teacher to visit, free of charge, before they bring a party, in order that they can plan a day trip.

Although there are only a few city farms in this book, they are to be found all over the country. Most of them belong to The National Federation of City Farms, The Old Vicarage, 66 Fraser Street, Windmill Hill, Bedminster, Bristol BS3 4LY. Drop them a line and they will tell you if there is one in your area. Many zoos belong to The National Federation of Zoological Gardens of Great Britain and Ireland, Zoological Gardens, Regent's Park, London NW1 4RY. The Federation does much good, all aimed at improving zoos in one way or another. Zoos are only able to join the Federation if they conform to standards and a Code of Practice. It played an important part in the work leading up to the Zoo Licensing Act 1981. It is the Federation that organises the two-year City and Guilds course in Animal Management for keepers (and others).

It costs a lot of money to run a zoo, which is why admission fees often seem inordinately high. What many visitors do not realise is the number of employees that a zoo has. Of course there are keepers, but there are also drivers and maintenance men, administrators and secretaries, cooks and waitresses, gate staff and paper pickers, and many others. If you take a sample admission fee of, say £4.60, one can take a look at how the money is spent. For a start the zoo has to pay 60p in VAT. Of the remaining £4, nearly £2 goes on wages and veterinary expenses. Food for the animals costs 60p, heating and lighting accounts for another 36p. The offices and advertising cost around 15p. Maintenance gobbles up a further 40p. Upkeep of the gardens, the vehicles and other bits and pieces use up the last 50p or so. Because of the costs many zoos run adoption schemes. The way they work is that the cost of maintaining each animal is calculated, and this is the cost of adoption. Members of the public are encouraged to pay that sum for a particular animal, and in return their name is displayed on the cage, they get regular newsletters and invitations to events and a variety of other rewards. Many people adopt animals in this way, and it helps the zoo's finances. Sometimes an adoption is arranged by a group of people or a family as a present for one of the members, and I think that is a lovely idea. Why don't you contact a zoo and enquire about adoption schemes?

To be sure, the cost of adopting a large animal is high, but you can adopt a duck or a python or whatever takes your fancy, and such a little beast will not cost you much. Sometimes businesses of one sort or another adopt animals, and one or two zoos have arranged effective corporate sponsorship deals with large companies. Why more firms do not take up this aspect of marketing, I cannot understand. One of the best is at Dublin Zoo which is sponsored by BISTO. Not only is the trade name to be found on all the literature, but there is a BISTO train that carries visitors around the park. The name is presented to millions of people in this way for a very modest outlay. Corporate sponsorship of zoos is a great idea and well worth looking into from both sides.

Some of the collections in this book are owned and run by local authorities. I think this is a marvellous idea. It seems to me that local authorities should be doing this sort of thing. After all, they are responsible for gardens and parks, all of which are part of the environment in which we live. I feel it is just not good enough for them to sweep the roads and provide car parks. Many councils cannot see what is in it for them, but the cost is not high for a small collection and the returns in goodwill and public relations are high. My own local authority is useless; they would not recognise a good marketing and public relations opportunity if it jumped up and hit them between the eyes. Having said all that, there are one or two local authority collections that the councils should be ashamed of. They are usually a few broken-down aviaries stuck away in a corner of the local park. While we are on the subject of parks, it should not be forgotten that parks are often great places for animals. Many of them that have an ornamental lake maintain collections of waterfowl, some of which are quite splendid. London's Regent's Park has a fair collection, and St James's Park has a wealth of birds, even including pelicans. An added advantage to keeping birds in this way is that they help to attract wild birds as well, and in St James's Park it is sometimes difficult to tell which birds are part of the collection and which are not. Kew Gardens has a good collection of waterfowl, and in both these places if you feel like sharing your sandwich with the birds you can be sure that in a very few seconds you will be surrounded by a whole gang of sparrows and pigeons and geese. Often the birds will sit happily on your hand.

When I sorted out the information for the zoo pages of this book, I found myself in a quandary as to the order in which they should be printed. In the end I thought that a geographical sequence might be best since someone who is planning a day out at a zoo probably thinks about the area first of all, whether this is within easy reach of home, or in the area around his holiday resort. However, I realise that this is not ideal so you will also find the collections listed alphabetically, and according to category as well. On each of the zoo pages you will discover various animal symbols. These are representations of the animals in the collection. That is not to say you will not find other animals as well, but the ones depicted represent the major interests of the collection in question. Another point to bear in mind is these generic animal drawings. If you think the picture of the bird looks like a parrot or an eagle or a duck, it does not mean that the collection is going to feature parrots or eagles or ducks. That symbol simply means BIRD, and the collection in question might house domestic fowl. The same applies to the other drawings; the symbol for MAMMAL might refer to Shire Horses, monkeys or lions. An explanation of the symbols is as follows:

   MAMMALS

   BIRDS

   REPTILES AND AMPHIBIANS

   INVERTEBRATES, both terrestrial and arboreal

   AQUATIC ANIMALS

Teachers might not be aware that many of the establishments listed in this book are quite happy to send a member of their education staff to schools. Usually such a person arrives with a selection of live animals which the children can watch and enjoy, and lessons like these are very popular and of considerable educational value, since there is a lot of difference between seeing an animal on the other side of a fence and seeing it only a metre or so from one's face in a familiar classroom where it has far more impact. Naturally enough, most places make a charge for this service, but some only ask for expenses, and in any case it is probably worth enquiring about.

The map in this book will enable you to see at a glance where the collections are located, and the numbers beside each location can be checked against the alphabetical list so that you can discover more about what is to be found in the area.

Bristol Zoo [1]

Clifton, Bristol, BS8 3HA
(On the A4176 opposite Durdham Downs)
Tel: 0272 738951
Proprietor: The Bristol and West of England
Zoological Society

Open: Every day except Christmas Day from 9.00 (10.00 on Sunday) until 5.00 to 6.00

Admission Fees: £3.20 adults, £1.60 children under 14 years. Party rates, which must be booked in advance and for a minimum number of 25: £2.60 adults and £1.30 children

Additional Costs: Parking 40p

Catering: The restaurant, and the bar where you can get snacks, are open all year. There are additional kiosks and a cafeteria in the summer

Facilities for Children: Children's meals are available

Facilities for the Disabled: Wheelchairs are available on request, there are toilets for the disabled, and most exhibits can be reached via ramps

Restrictions: No dogs or unaccompanied children. Feeding of the animals is prohibited

Bristol is a lovely little zoo. At one time the enclosures were all Victorian, which was interesting, but pretty grim for the animals. Nowadays most have been redesigned and rebuilt, and as a result are infinitely better. The Monkey Temple has been retained, however, and it works very well for the colony of Crab Eating Macaques that live in it. The Polar Bear enclosure remains an embarrassment to everyone, not least to Bristol Zoo. The collection is comprehensive and fascinating, and Bristol takes education seriously, and their breeding record is impressive, especially perhaps with primates and Okapi. This zoo contains the most comprehensive collection of pigeons in the country. There are plenty of indoor attractions which you can view when it is raining, and there is a full programme of events during the year, many for children.

St Werburgh's City Farm [2]

Watercress Road, St Werburgh's Road, Bristol, BS2 9YJ
(220 yards (200 m) past St Werburgh's Parish Church)
Tel: 0272 428241
Proprietor: St Werburgh's City Farm Ltd, which is a charity

Open: Every day from 9.00 to 6.00

Admission Fees: None, but donations are gratefully received

Additional Costs: None

Catering: There is a cafe/restaurant

Facilities for Children: Children's meals are available. Children can feed the animals, and there is a children's worker on the farm

Facilities for the Disabled: There are two suitable toilets for the disabled, raised flower beds, and where necessary, ramps

Restrictions: No dogs are allowed, nor bicycles, and no alcoholic drinks or smoking is permitted

Bristol is a pretty amazing place for small conservation and self-help groups — I do not know anywhere better — and this farm is among the best of them. It actually produces food that you can buy, including yoghurt, and the food served in the cafeteria is wholefood. The farm has a range of traditional farm animals and specialises in the more unusual breeds. There are actually five parts to this farm: the main site at Watercress Road houses the animals, a horticultural therapy unit and a children's playground. On Ashley Hill there is an allotment with two greenhouses. On a footpath between there and Mina Road there is a nature garden created by schools, and there is a 5-acre (2-ha) site at Narroways Junction.

The whole place was a derelict site that has been converted into a working farm. Working with, and actually touching animals is encouraged, and there is a development officer who is responsible for children with special needs; and there is also a schoolroom for educational visits.

Windmill Hill City Farm [3]

38a Doveton Street, Bedminster, Bristol, BS3 4DU
(From the main East Street in Bedminster turn into Philip Street,
which is opposite the Asda building)
Tel: 0272 633252
Proprietor: Windmill Hill City Farm Ltd, which is a charitable
company

Open: Every day from 8.00 till dusk

Admission Fees: None, except for guided tours in which case 50p per
person is charged

Additional Costs: None for the general visitor, but see below for
information about Education Fortnights

Catering: There is a cafe

Facilities for Children: There is a splendidly entitled Rumpus Room, a play
centre and an under-sevens adventure area, and children's meals are available

Facilities for the Disabled: At the moment there is limited access, but this is
being improved

Restrictions: No dogs or other pets are allowed except for guide dogs, and
unaccompanied children are not admitted

This is a working city farm where one can find a wide variety of farm
animals including Jacob's Sheep, Soay Sheep and a Gloucester Old Spot
Pig. There is an education room and a nature reserve, and what I like
particularly is the idea of the Education Fortnights that are run at this
farm. They hold them three or four times a year, and on each day
during the fortnight they can accommodate a school group during which
pupils are given the chance to do something that is not only interesting
but is actually useful, such as making yoghurt, or some other activity.
The charge for this is a very modest 75p per person. Lovely idea!

Child Beale Wildlife Park [4]

Church Farm, Lower Basildon, Reading, Berkshire, RG8 9NH

(On the A329 from Pangbourne to Oxford. The park can also be reached by boat from the River Thames)

Tel: 0491 671325 or 07357 5171 or 07357 5172
Proprietor: The Child Beale Wildlife Trust

Open: Every day from mid-March to the end of September

Admission Fees: £2.00 adults, £1 children, OAPs and disabled visitors. £35.00 for pre-booked coaches, or £40.00 if not booked. Car parking is free

Additional Costs: Train ride

Catering: Ice cream, cold and hot drinks, and sweets are all available

Facilities for Children: The nicest, best adventure playground in the world — well worth visiting just for that. A good paddling pool as well. There is a pets corner

Facilities for the Disabled: There are ramps, invalid chairs, special toilets and shelters for the disabled

Restrictions: No dogs allowed, except in the car park where they must be kept on a lead

This is a delightful and extraordinary little collection of birds and rare breeds of domestic animals. Many of them have been bred in the park and the mammals are shown, and win prizes at agricultural shows. There is an education officer and lecture room, and in addition to the animals the place is worth a visit to see the buildings and statuary in the grounds. In the Tropical House one can admire a variety of tropical fish, amphibians, birds and insects.

Windsor Safari Park [5]

Winkfield Road, Windsor, Berkshire, SL4 4AY
(2 miles (3 km) from Windsor on the B3022 Windsor to Ascot road.
From the M4 leave at Junction 3, from the M3 leave at Junction 3,
and from the M25, Junction 13)
Tel: 0753 869841
Proprietor: Southbrook and City Holdings Ltd

Open: Every day, except Christmas Day, from 10.00

Admission Fees: £5.95 adults, £4.95 children under 14 years and OAPs.
Party rates when there are over 12 in a vehicle: £4.50 adults, £3.50 children
and OAPs. School rates: £2.40 children — one adult is admitted free with
every 10 children. Additional adults are charged £3.50

Additional Costs: None

Catering: There are fast food cafeterias, licensed bars and refreshment kiosks

Facilities for Children: There is a large playground, a rainbow soft play
centre, a Noah's Ark adventure play centre, a children's zoo and a tropical
world

Facilities for the Disabled: There are special toilets, and most areas have
ramps for easy access

Restrictions: None

There are all sorts here. Seven drive-through reserves hold Giraffes,
zebras, antelopes, wolves, deer, elephants, Tigers, lions, baboons,
bears and other animals. In addition there are dolphins and parrot shows
and butterflies. The park has succeeded in breeding dolphins and
Sunbitterns. For teachers there is a purpose built education centre with
a lecture room and a natural history museum offering a range of audio-
visual and video presentations. A qualified education officer is available
for guided tours. There are worksheets and teachers' packs available on
request.

When you have finished looking at animals you can enjoy the twin-track
Alpine Toboggan Run (if you have that sort of stomach), the boating
lake and the children's playgrounds.

Stagsden Bird Gardens [6]

Stagsden, Bedfordshire, MK43 8SL
(Stagsden village is 15 miles (24 km) west of Bedford on the A422)
Tel: 02302 2745
Proprietors: Mr and Mrs R.E. Rayment

Open: Every day from 11.00 to 6.00, or dusk in winter

Admission Fees: £1.50 adults, 70p children under 16 years, £1.30 OAPs.
Enquire about party rates

Additional Costs: None

Catering: There is a kiosk selling hot drinks, ice cream and sweets, or one
can picnic in the area set aside

Facilities for Children: None

Facilities for the Disabled: Flat surfaces and wide gateways make for easy
access by wheelchairs

Restrictions: No dogs are allowed, and nor is the feeding of the birds

This was one of the very first bird gardens in the country. It was the
first to breed Hume's Bar Tailed Pheasant in captivity, and although
there are other pheasants in the collection as well as a wide variety of
other birds, the establishment is now concentrating on cranes and are
seeking to establish a world crane-breeding centre. Like all other
wildlife cranes are disappearing from the wild, and it is a real pleasure to
find someone conserving them. There are also Sacred Ibis, parrots,
birds of prey and waterfowl, and when you have seen the birds there is
an attractive rose garden to enjoy. Questionnaire factsheets are
available for teachers, and there is a small exhibition relevant to the
work that is being done.

Whipsnade Park Zoo [7]

The Zoological Society of London, Whipsnade Park, Dunstable, Bedfordshire, LU6 2LF
(On the B4540, some 4 miles (6½ km) northwest of Junction 9 of the M1)
Tel: 0582 872171
Proprietor: The Zoological Society of London

Open: Every day except Christmas Day from 10.00 to 6.00 (7.00 on Sundays and Bank Holidays, sunset in the winter)

Admission Fees: £3.50 adults, £1.80 for children under 16 (or free if under 5), £1.80 OAPs, £2.70 students. The party rate is £2.70 adults, £1.40 children (minimum number: 20)

Additional Costs: If you wish to take your car into the zoo it will cost £3.00, except in July, August and on Bank Holidays when it is £4.00. Otherwise parking in the car park is free. Rides on the steam train or the road train are extra

Catering: There is a central cafeteria and five kiosks

Facilities for Children: Children's meals are available, and there are pushchairs. Children's Zoo

Facilities for the Disabled: Toilets are available for the disabled. Much of the park is easily accessible for wheelchairs, but some areas are certainly not

Restrictions: No dogs, and feeding of animals is not allowed

Whipsnade is the country home of London Zoo, and quite unlike anywhere else. Most animals are in herds in very roomy enclosures, and 96 per cent of the mammals were born in the park. Several species are at liberty so you might well find yourself sharing a picnic with a peafowl or a Bennett's Wallaby. Whipsnade is a super day out, but tiring, as there are over 500 acres (200 ha) to cover. On the Downs within the zoo is the famous White Lion — not a live animal, but cut into the chalk. It doesn't look like a lion when you are walking along its tail, but drive over to Ivinghoe and you can see it clearly. Many endangered species have been bred, such as Père David's Deer, Przewalski's Horse and Cheetah. Early on a misty autumn morning the park is lovely. The Red Deer stags bell loudly, the cranes give vent to eerie calls, and the sheep throw themselves at each other in stylised combat so that the crash of their heads meeting can be heard long before you see them.

Woburn Wild Animal Kingdom [8]

Woburn Park, Woburn, Bedfordshire, MK17 9QN
(2 miles (3 km) from Woburn village)
Tel: 0525 290407
Proprietor: The Chipperfield Organisation

Open: Every day from the beginning of March till the end of October from 10.00 to 5.00

Admission Fees: Cars: £5 adults, £4 children and OAPs. Coaches: £4.50 adults, £2.50 children from 4 to 15 years, £3.50 OAPs

Additional Costs: None

Catering: There is a restaurant and ice cream stalls

oburn Wild Animal Kingdom afari and Leisure Park

L-inclusive charge —) hidden extras

ults £5.00, Senior Citizens, £4.00
ildren (4-5 years) £4.00

"hink that this is the best bargain -out that I know"

adian Timber Wolves & Parrot Shows
tains Largest drive-through Safari Park
e mile return journey Sky Ride
senger Railway Carousel Ghost Train
ter-Skelter Pet's Corner Rainbow Ride
a-lion Shows Children's Veteran Car Rides
ating Lakes Tiger Bouncer Elephant Displays
rot Shows
ecial Rates for Coach & School parties
en Every Day at 10.00 am (Last entry 5.00pm)

quiries:
lephone: Woburn (0525) 290407
PEN 11 MARCH to 29 OCTOBER 1989

Facilities for Children: There is a pets corner, a variety of rides including a set of traditional gallopers, and children's meals can be bought in the restaurant

Facilities for the Disabled: There are ramps, and toilets for the disabled

Restrictions: No dogs are admitted, nor unaccompanied children. Feeding animals is forbidden, and so are soft-top cars for obvious reasons

This 300-acre (121-ha) safari park was opened in 1970 and today is the largest drive-through wild animal collection in Britain. Each year about half a million people visit Woburn. The collection consists almost entirely of mammals, every species of which breeds here apart from the elephants, and there are hopes that even they might soon do so. Most of the animals are the standard large mammals, but there are some particularly interesting species such as the Wisent, or European Bison from Poland, where it is almost extinct. There is also the only breeding group of Bongo in the country. Bongo are exquisite antelopes which are endangered. They breed in the park. Deer have always been important at Woburn, long before anyone thought of safari parks, and in the story of the extraordinary Père David's Deer, they and Woburn have had a long association. The story of this species is fascinating, and if you don't know it, it is well worth looking up in any number of books, or briefly in the Woburn Safari Park guide book. Educational leaflets are available on request.

Waddesdon Manor [9]

Aylesbury, Buckinghamshire, HP18 0JH
(6 miles (10 km) from Aylesbury on the A41 to Bicester)
Tel: 0296 651211
Proprietor: The National Trust

Open: From the end of March until late October from 1.00 to 5.00 each week from Wednesday to Sunday, though at weekends in May and through to September, the aviary closes at 6.00. On Good Friday, and on Bank Holidays the times of opening are from 11.00 to 6.00. During November and December it is open on Saturdays and Sundays from 12.00 to 5.00

Admission Fees: £1.50 adults, 75p children from 5 to 17 years, except in November and December when admission is free

Additional Costs: Admission to the house is extra

Catering: A licensed restaurant is open during visiting hours

Facilities for Children: There is a play area

Facilities for the Disabled: The collection is accessible by wheelchair, and there are toilets for the disabled

Restrictions: Dogs must be kept on a lead. Deer and birds must not be fed

Baron Ferdinand de Rothschild built the aviary at Waddesdon Manor in 1889. It is semicircular with the wings divided into separate flights. Over the years a number of species have been bred, some of them endangered. Such breeding involves species such as parrots, fruit pigeons, Spreo Starlings, and Rothschild's Grackles. One can also see the small herd of Japanese Sika Deer in two enclosures in the grounds. There are various sculptures around the grounds, and one can visit the house, which is that of Baron Ferdinand de Rothschild. The house contains collections of lace, buttons and fans.

Appleby Castle
Conservation Centre [10]

Appleby in Westmoreland, Cumbria, CA16 6XH
(12 miles (19 km) southeast of Penrith on the A66 in the
centre of Appleby)
Tel: 07683 51402
Proprietor: Ferguson Industrial Holdings PLC

Open: Every day between 23 March and 1 October from 10.00 to 5.00

Admission Fees: £2.00 adults, £1.00 children under 16 years, £1.00 OAPs.
Party rate for groups of over 20 is £1.50 adults, 75p children and OAPs

Additional Costs: None

Catering: Tea rooms serve coffee, lunch and tea, together with ice cream
and soft drinks

Facilities for Children: There is a Tarzan Trail and a nature trail. One can
also get a history worksheet and a bird and animal quiz

Facilities for the Disabled: Many of the paths are level and suitable for
wheelchairs, and one toilet is suitable for the disabled

Restrictions: Dogs must be kept on a lead at all times, and no
unaccompanied children are admitted

This is an attractive collection. It is the seventh Rare Breeds Survival
Trust centre and supports a number of rare breeds of domestic farm
animals together with a large collection of waterfowl, pheasants, poultry
and owls, together with some parrots and small birds. Five rare breeds
of sheep are bred each year, as are Bagot Goats and numbers of birds.
There is a nature trail and educational leaflets are available. The keep of
the castle is open to visitors and contains much of interest. One can also
admire pottery from the Nanking Cargo of porcelain, the gardens, and
the River Eden.

Bridgemere Wildlife Park [11]

Bridgemere, Nantwich, Cheshire
(Just off the A51 between Woore and Nantwich)
Tel: 09365 223
Proprietor: Bridgemere Nurseries Ltd

Open: Every day from 10.00 to 6.00

Admission Fees: £1.50 adults, £1.00 children over 4 years of age, £1.00 OAPs

Additional Costs: None stated

Catering: There is a coffee shop serving drinks and light snacks

Facilities for Children: There is an adventure playground

Facilities for the Disabled: All areas are accessible to wheelchairs

41

Restrictions: No dogs are allowed, and the feeding of animals is permitted only with certain species, and then only with food provided by the park

Bridgemere Wildlife Park was bought by the present proprietor in April 1988, and it is undergoing major redevelopment. The collection specialises in waterfowl, various species of deer, and a number of rare breeds of farm animals, and if you think one farm animal looks much like another, think again, for the variety is astonishing. The lecture room should be completed by the middle of 1989. Educational leaflets are available for school groups, and slide shows and lectures are available if booked in advance.

Chester Zoo [12]

Upton by Chester, Chester, CH2 1LH
(Just off the A41, 2 miles (3 km) north of the city
centre)
Tel: 0244 380280
Proprietor: The North of England Zoological
Society

Open: 10.00 to dusk all year; closed Christmas Day

Admission Fees: £3.50 adults, £1.75 children under 15 years and OAPs.
Party rates for groups of 16 or more are £3.00 adults, £1.50 children. These
are prices for 1988; those for 1989 have not been fixed at the time of writing

Additional Costs: Boat rides 60p. Car parking is free

Catering: There is more than one cafeteria, a restaurant and various ice
cream stalls

Facilities for Children: There are mother and baby rooms, pushchairs may
be hired, children's meals are available, and there is a children's farm and play
area. How pleasing it is to find somewhere that takes children really seriously

Facilities for the Disabled: Invalid chairs are available, and there are ramps
to exhibits. There are plenty of suitable toilets

Restrictions: No dogs are allowed, nor feeding of the animals. Children
should be supervised

Pat Cade, the public relations officer, says that Chester Zoo is generally recognised as one of Europe's finest zoos, and that is a description no-one who knows the place could argue with. It is the biggest collection in Britain after London, with a formidable reputation for breeding animals. The scope of the collection ranges from large mammals at one end to small invertebrates at the other. I defy you not to be excited by Chester Zoo, and when you have looked at the animals there are 110 acres (45 ha) of prize-winning gardens. When the zoo was extensively renovated twenty or so years ago, the horticultural staff became so adept at their work, persuading the most reluctant plants to grow, that a legend grew up about them. It was said that if they tried hard enough they could even grow trees from matchsticks. That is the sort of zoo it is. It would need a book to list the highlights of the collection; go and see for yourself. As you might imagine, education is regarded as most important, and there is an extensive education department with a wide range of facilities.

Linton Zoological Gardens [13]

Hadstock Road, Linton, Cambridgeshire
(10 miles (16 km) southeast of Cambridge along the
B1052, just off the A604)
Tel: 0223 891308
Proprietors: L.G., D.J. and K.C. Simmons

Open: Every day except Christmas Day from 10.00 to 6.30 in summer, and till dusk in winter

Admission Fees: £2.20 adults, 90p children over two years. Enquire about party rates for groups of 20 or more

Additional Costs: None

Catering: There is a cafeteria which is open only during the summer

Facilities for Children: None stated

Facilities for the Disabled: Full facilities for the disabled are available

Restrictions: Dogs are restricted to the car park, unaccompanied children are not admitted, and there is no feeding of the animals allowed

It is interesting how many people who work avidly for conservation started life in some sort of business that the world at large might think was incompatible with the subject. Linton Zoo started when the owners closed their pet shops and moved their collection here. Since then it has grown and nowadays it fills 10½ acres (4¼ ha) of attractively landscaped gardens. There are plenty of mammals and birds to see, as well as Axolotls, reptiles of various species, and invertebrates. Conservation is regarded as very important, and they have bred Bengal Eagle Owls, Toco Toucans, Snapping Turtles, Seychelles Palm Spiders and millipedes, and Binturongs. Worksheets and talks can be had on request.

The Wildfowl Trust [14]

Peakirk, Peterborough, PE6 7NP
(5 miles (8 km) north of Peterborough leave the A15 at Glinton,
then travel east along the B1443)
Tel: 0733 252271
Proprietor: The Wildfowl Trust

Open: Every day except Christmas Eve and Christmas Day from 9.30 to 5.30
in summer, and till one hour before dusk in winter

Admission Fees: (1988) £2.20 adults, 90p children between 4 and 16 years,
£1.30 OAPs. Party rates for groups of 20 or more: £1.50. Enquire about
special rates for school parties

Additional Costs: None

Catering: There is a restaurant that is open from Easter until August, and
refreshments are available throughout the year

Facilities for Children: There are level paths for pushchairs, and children
may feed the birds

Facilities for the Disabled: There are free wheelchairs available, suitable
toilet facilities, and the paths are level

Restrictions: No dogs are allowed into the reserve

A favourite with photographers, the gardens at Peakirk are a beautiful combination of woodland and water, 5 miles (8 km) from Peterborough. The gardens occupy the site of an old osier bed through which passed the ancient Car Dyke. In Roman times this was one of the most important waterways of East Anglia. Today it is full of waterfowl — almost 700 of them, some very rare. Among the special attractions are the Chilean Flamingoes, the Black Necked and the Coscoroba Swans, and the Andean Geese. Trumpeter Swans descended from a group presented by the Queen also breed regularly here. Talks and visual aid presentations can be arranged, and various materials are available for teachers.

The Wildfowl Trust [15]

Pintail House, Hundred Foot Bank, Welney, Wisbech, Cambridgeshire, PE14 9TN
(Take the A1101 Welney to Littleport road to the first bridge, then follow the road along the New Bedford River)
Tel: 0353 860711
Proprietor: The Wildfowl Trust

Open: Every day except Christmas Eve and Christmas Day from 10.00 to 5.00, or one hour before dusk in winter. Evening visits can be arranged throughout the year

Admission Fees: (1988) £1.70 adults, 90p children between 4 and 16 years, £1.30 OAPs. Party rate for groups of 20 or more: £1.20. Enquire about rates for school parties

Additional Costs: None

Catering: There is a tea room

Facilities for Children: There is a nature trail in summer

Facilities for the Disabled: There is a suitable toilet, and access to the main observatory

Restrictions: No dogs are allowed into the reserve, and all visitors must report to reception on arrival

At Welney Reserve the visitor can expect to see a spectacular number of birds. Covering 850 acres (344 ha), the reserve lies between the Old and New Bedford Rivers. In times of flood the water off the fens drains down these two seventeenth-century channels to create a huge reservoir. This is a successfully managed refuge for large numbers of swans and ducks in winter, especially Bewick's and Whooper Swans, Wigeon, Tufted Duck, Pochard and Pintail Ducks. Talks and guided tours can be arranged, and worksheets can be provided for teachers and school groups.

Newquay Zoo [16]

Trevance Park, Newquay, Cornwall
(within Trevance Leisure Park)
Tel: 0637 873342
Proprietor: Restormel Borough Council

Open: Every day from April to October from 10.00 to 4.30

Admission Fees: £2.30 adults, £1.30 children under 15 years, £1.30 OAPs.
Party rate for groups of ten or over is £1.80

Additional Costs: Car parking is 60p

Catering: There is a cafeteria and an ice cream stall

Facilities for Children: There is a maze, a Tarzan Trail and an adventure playground

Facilities for the Disabled: There are ramps, and wheelchairs are available

Restrictions: No dogs are allowed

This is a small, municipal collection containing parrots, big cats, reptiles, primates and others. There is an education centre and an education officer. Macaws, and more interestingly Diana Monkeys, have been bred here.

Padstow Tropical Bird Gardens [17]

Fentonluna Lane, Padstow, Cornwall, PL28 8BB
(In the old quarter of Padstow on the B3276)
Tel: 0841 532262
Proprietors: D.J.L. and P. Brown

Open: Every day except Christmas Day from 10.30. The last admission in summer is at 7.00, and in winter at 4.00

Admission Fees: £2.00 adults, £1.00 children under 16 years, £1.50 OAPs. Party rates for groups of 20 or over are 20% off the normal rates

Additional Costs: None stated

Catering: There is a tea room which is open only between Easter and the end of September

Facilities for Children: None stated

Facilities for the Disabled: None stated

Restrictions: Dogs are only admitted on a lead, and feeding the animals is forbidden

This really is a very nice collection. There are plenty of familiar species to be seen, together with many that most people will not have come across previously. Breeding successes are formidable, with forty species having reproduced here — many for the first time in the country. Some of the species breed fairly readily, such as the Chinese Painted Quail (when you can persuade the hens to take the matter seriously and not to regard the laying of eggs as merely a treasure hunt), but some of the results are spectacular. The spectacular Taccazze Sunbird and the diminutive Fairy Blue Wren are two such. In addition to the birds, the gardens are marvellous, and many species of plants have been established as foodplants for butterflies. You can also see Butterfly World, an exhibition of the world's most colourful and interesting butterflies and moths. This is also one of the few places these days where you can find Choughs, the bird that is regarded as the emblem of Cornwall, though alas these appealing little crows are now extinct in the West Country.

Paradise Park [18]

Hayle, St Ives, Cornwall
Tel: 0736 753365
Proprietor: Mike Reynolds

Open: Every day from 10.00 till 6.00 from May to 11 September, and till 4.00 in winter. The gates close two hours later

Admission Fees: £2.50 adults, £1.50 children from 4 to 14 years, £2.00 OAPs

Additional Costs: None

Catering: There is a cafeteria and a restaurant

Facilities for Children: Children's meals are available

Facilities for the Disabled: Wheelchairs and toilets are available, and there are ramps where appropriate

Restrictions: Dogs must remain in the car park

Paradise Park says it has two main tasks. The first is to breed rare and endangered species from around the world, and second to help save species of special interest to Cornwall, such as otters, Choughs and Merlins. No less than 77 different species of animal have been bred here, and the collection specialises in parrots, cranes, penguins and otters. But if you don't like those animals don't stay away, for there are plenty of others. There are magnificent King Vultures, three species of eagle as well as falcons, hawks and owls, some of which you can watch being flown at artificial lures during the falconry displays. There are five enclosures of otters, and a free 'Save the Otter' badge for every child. There are small cuddly animals such as lambs that you can meet and make friends with, and teachers can obtain literature from the education officer. Paradise Park also has its own pub and brewery, and amusements and a miniature railway so that you can take the weight off your feet for a while.

Riber Castle Wildlife Park [19]

Riber Castle, Matlock, Derbyshire, DE4 5JU
(Take the A615 from Matlock to Tansley, then Alsers Lane for 1 mile
(1½ km) to Riber. It is 6 miles (10 km) from Junction 28 on the M1)
Tel: 0629 582073
Proprietors: Mr and Mrs Williams

Open: Every day except Christmas Day from 10.00

Admission Fees: £2.50 adults, £1.50 children under 16 years. Enquire about party rates

Additional Costs: None

Catering: There is a cafeteria that is open every day, together with a licensed bar that is open only between Easter and October, or by arrangement. Ice cream and sweets may be obtained from the gift shop

Facilities for Children: Children's meals may be obtained

Facilities for the Disabled: There is a toilet for the disabled, and there are ramps to most areas

Restrictions: No dogs are allowed, and it is forbidden to cross safety barriers

A small collection of animals which includes the most comprehensive collection of lynx in the world. Animals bred here have been released into the Vosges Mountains in France in 1983. In 1987 for the first time anywhere a Siberian Lynx gave birth to quins. There is an education officer, and short talks can be arranged.

Buckfast Butterfly Farm [20]

Buckfastleigh Steam and Leisure Park, Buckfastleigh, Devon, TQ11 0DZ
(Just off the A38 Exeter to Plymouth trunk road at Dart Bridge junction)
Tel: 0364 42916
Proprietor: D.J. Field

Open: Every day from Good Friday to the end of October from 10.00 to 5.30

Admission Fees: Enquire about current prices as these change periodically

Additional Costs: None

Catering: There is a cafe at the Dart Valley Steam Railway, about 330 yards (300 m) away

Facilities for Children: None

Facilities for the Disabled: Ramps are provided

Restrictions: No dogs allowed except for guide dogs

There are plenty of exotic and beautiful butterflies to be seen at Buckfast Butterfly Farm, and from an educational point of view there is a full package available including teachers' notes. There are lecture room facilities, and guided tours with a knowledgeable entomologist can be arranged. About twenty exotic butterflies and moths are bred regularly. For steam buffs in the family, the Dart Valley railway is next door, and the whole area is full of good things to see and do.

Exmoor Bird Gardens [21]

South Stowford, Bratton Fleming, Barnstaple, North Devon, EX31 4SG
(On the B3226 between Bratton Fleming and Blackmoor Gate)
Tel: 05983 352 or 05983 412
Proprietor: C. Clark

Open: Every day from 10.00 to 6.00 in the summer, and till 4.00 in winter

Admission Fees: (1989) £2.50 adults, £1.25 children between 3 and 16 years,
£2.25 OAPs. Party rates for groups of 20 or more: £2.10 adults, £1.00 children

Additional Costs: None

Catering: There is a restaurant and an ice cream kiosk

Facilities for Children: Children's meals are available, and there is a baby changing area

Facilities for the Disabled: All areas are accessible with wheelchairs, there are toilets for the disabled, and ramps to the restaurant

Restrictions: No pets are allowed

Though this is called a bird garden, as so often happens there are plenty of mammals as well. To give you an idea of what is to be seen, some of the animals are Toco Toucans, Humboldt Penguins, Red Breasted Geese, cockatoos, Vietnamese Pot Bellied Pigs, Fulvous Ducks, chipmunks and Cape Barren Geese. Green Naped Lorikeets, Bennett's Wallabies, Guanacos, African Ringnecked Parakeets, Golden Mantled Rosella Parakeets, the pigs, Pigmy Goats and Cheer Pheasants have all been bred. The enclosures are all large and there are animals that the visitor can meet and touch, and even feed.

Paignton Aquarium [22]

South Quay, Paignton Harbour, Paignton, Devon
(55 yards (50 m) along South Quay)
Tel: 0803 522913
Proprietor: L.A.J. Jackman

Open: Every day between Easter and the end of September, from 10.00

Admission Fees: 65p adults, 35p children under 14 years, 35p OAPs.
Enquire about party rates

Additional Costs: None. There is a multi-storey car park next door

Catering: There is a restaurant above

Facilities for Children: None

Facilities for the Disabled: In response to this question, the answer given is 'OK'

Restrictions: No feeding of the fish is allowed

This is a collection of local seashore life, explained with educational and conservation displays.

Shaldon Wildlife Trust [23]

Ness Drive, Shaldon, Devon, TQ14 0HP
(Off the A379 Torquay to Teignmouth road)
Tel: 0626 872234
Proprietor: Shaldon Wildlife Trust Ltd

Open: From April to September daily between 10.00 and 6.00, and during the winter from 11.00 to 4.00. (It is best to telephone to confirm these winter times if you are travelling any distance)

Admission Fees: £1.25 adults, 75p children under 14 years, 75p OAPs. Enquire about party rates

Additional Costs: None. There is a large Council car park opposite

Catering: None

Facilities for Children: None

Facilities for the Disabled: Mentally and physically handicapped visitors are admitted free of charge, but wheelchair access is difficult

Restrictions: No dogs are allowed, and no public feeding of the animals

The Trust maintains a specialist collection of rare and endangered species of small mammals and exotic birds and reptiles including monkeys, parrots, owls and snakes, in a woodland setting. The only animals kept are bred in captivity, and most of the current stock is involved in breeding programmes linked with other collections. Some of the most interesting species are marmosets and tamarins, lemurs, Agoutis and Acouchis. Lectures are given to organised parties.

Abbotsbury Swannery [24]

New Barn Road, Abbotsbury, Dorset
(1 mile (1½ km) past the church and the tithe barn in Abbotsbury)
Tel: 0305 871684
Proprietor: Strangways and Holland House Estates

Open: From mid-May to mid-September from 9.30 to 5.00 every day

Admission Fees: £1.20 adults and children, £1.00 OAPs. Party rate if booked in advance is 10% off the price for groups of ten or more

Additional Costs: Pony or horse and trap rides cost 40p adults, 20p children, 35p OAPs

Catering: Nothing

Facilities for Children: None

Facilities for the Disabled: All areas can be reached with the Swannery's wheelchair, and the hide has a built-in area for it

Restrictions: No dogs allowed, and please do not feed the swans

This is not a collection or a zoo, but a free herd of Mute Swans who nest in a unique fashion and have done so at this site for at least 600 years. It is the only colonial herd of these birds that can be visited at nesting time. The swans are an incredible sight, and if you are in the area you really ought to go and see them, but in addition the area is a Wetland of international importance and many birds nest on its 8-mile (13-km) stretch, including a colony of rare Little Terns. There is an ancient decoy pond, with explanatory model to show how it worked. There is also a small herb garden, and wild plants are labelled. Before you leave the area you ought not to miss the extraordinarily beautiful village of Abbotsbury, which is rich in history.

The Great Shire Horse Centre [25]

Lodmoor Country Park, Weymouth, Dorset
(½ mile (¾ km) from Weymouth Esplanade)
Tel: 0305 775315
Proprietor: R.P. Walpole

Open: Every day from Easter till the end of September from 10.00 to 5.00

Admission Fees: £1.75 adults, £1.25 children under 14 but free if under 3 years. Party rate: £1.45 adults, £1.25 children and OAPs, minimum number to qualify for these rates is 15. These figures are for 1988 only

Additional Costs: Car parking in the municipal car park. Wagon rides are 20p

Catering: None, but these are available in the municipal car park, and the pass out system allows re-entry throughout the day

Facilities for Children: There is a small pets area

Facilities for the Disabled: Passage ways are wide enough to allow for wheelchairs

Restrictions: No feeding of animals, and dogs are allowed only if they are on leads

Everyone loves shire horses, and this is a great place to meet them. You can watch demonstrations of harnessing, mane-plaiting and all sorts of other activities. There is also an aviary, and displays of agricultural machinery, drays and farm wagons and much else. In bad weather the demonstrations are under cover, and teachers can obtain project sheets for educational visits. Within Lodmoor Country Park are a variety of other attractions, such as a Butterfly Farm, a Sea Life Centre, a Leisure Ranch, a Nature Reserve and a Model World, and during the course of a day one can come and go between them; a great day out.

Lyme Regis Marine Aquarium [26]

The Cobb, Lyme Regis, Dorset
(Located in the old warehouse on the harbour wall)
Tel: 02974 3678
Proprietors: K.R. and J.B. Gollop

Open: Every day from May to October from 10.00 to 5.00, or till dusk during July and August

Admission Fees: 70p adults, 35p children under 15 years, 30p for members of school parties

Additional Costs: None

Catering: None

Facilities for Children: None

Facilities for the Disabled: Wheelchairs may be borrowed

Restrictions: None

This collection is an exhibition of local marine life, and if that sounds dull, don't you believe it. There are hosts of fascinating animals that live beneath the surface of the water, that for the most part we never see. This collection has been here for 30 years and is well worth looking at. You will never view plaice and chips in the same way again. The aquarium has its own boat, the *Donna Marie*, in which you can go for a short trip.

Worldwide Butterflies and Lullingstone Silk Farm [27]

Compton House, Sherborne, Dorset, DT9 4QN
(On the A30 midway between Yeovil and Sherborne)
Tel: 0935 74608
Proprietors: Mr and Mrs Robert Gooden

Open: Every day between 10.00 and 5.00 from April till 30 October

Admission Fees: £2.65 adults, £1.50 children, £1.95 OAPs. Party rate for groups of not less than 30 is £2.00

Additional Costs: None

Catering: There is a restaurant, and one may also buy ice cream and confectionery

Facilities for Children: None stated

Facilities for the Disabled: None stated

Restrictions: No dogs or unaccompanied children are allowed

Worldwide Butterflies has always been special to me, since many years ago I bought from this company several species of the first invertebrates that I ever kept, though I seem to remember that they came through a now long-defunct supplier of biological supplies in Newdigate. At Worldwide you can see butterflies and moths flying in their own jungles and in the palm house, or in the Tropicana outside. Conservation is of paramount importance here, and considerable work has been done on a variety of species including the Large Blue Butterfly. The farm specialises in species that can be reared at home and in schools, and much breeding takes place every year. Work sheets are available, and larvae and pupae may be bought. The silk farm part of the operation has supplied unique English silk for the last two coronations, for the Queen's wedding dress and for many other royal occasions including the wedding of the Princess of Wales. One can watch the process of preparing silk, either in reality or on videotape.

Bentley Wildfowl and Motor Museum [28]

Halland, Lewes, East Sussex, BN8 5AF
(1½ miles (2½ km) from the A22 and the A26, 7 miles (11 km)
northeast of Lewes)
Tel: 082584 573
Proprietor: East Sussex County Council

Open: Every day between 18 March and 31 October from 10.30 to 4.30 (or 5.00 in July and August)

Admission Fees: (1988) £2.50 adults, £1.20 children under 16 years, £1.50 OAPs, and there is a discount of 10% for parties of more than 10

Additional Costs: Train rides on summer Sundays

Catering: There is a tea room serving light lunches and cream teas

Facilities for Children: None stated

Facilities for the Disabled: There are ramps where necessary

Restrictions: No dogs are allowed

This is a splendid collection of over 100 species of waterfowl including several that are rare, most especially the White Winged Wood Duck that has bred so that specimens were returned to the wilds of Thailand whence they originally came. The reserve covers 23 acres (9 ha), and has much of interest. There is an education officer, two rooms for schools, and slide talks can be arranged. Worksheets and workbooks are available. This collection houses every species of swan in the world, and when you have had enough of birds there is the motor museum to visit, or the woodland walk, or any one of the super gardens.

Brighton Aquarium and Dolphinarium [29]

Madeira Drive, Marine Parade, Brighton, BN2 1TB
(On the sea front in the centre of Brighton)
Tel: 0273 604233 or 604234 or 671466
Proprietor: Aquarium Entertainments Ltd

Open: Every day between 10.00 and 5.15 during the summer and school holidays and at weekends, and every weekday during the winter from 10.00 to 4.15

Admission Fees: £2.40 adults and children over 3 years. Party rate: £2.00 adults, £1.30 per person on schools visits. The minimum number in a party is 15

Additional Costs: A simulator ride costs £1. There are parking meters and 'pay and display' car parks on the sea front

Catering: There is a cafeteria as well as ice cream and popcorn stalls, and at lunch time there is a bar

Facilities for Children: Children's meals are available, and there is a pram park

Facilities for the Disabled: Ramps make it possible to go everywhere

Restrictions: No dogs are allowed, and no feeding of the animals

There are hundreds of fish here from exotic reef species to Piranhas, Pike and Perch, together with plenty of aquatic invertebrates. There is also a collection of sharks, and a family of dolphins — the baby was born here. Other mammals are seals and sealions, and reptiles in the form of crocodiles. The building that the collection is housed in is worth seeing, and next door is a children's multi-activity centre called Pirates Deep (0273 674549). Dolphin and sealion shows are held daily. There is an education officer and a lecture room, and information leaflets and slide talks can be arranged. The Aquarium is keen on conservation in an age when most people don't give a thought to what lives beneath the sea unless it is to be eaten.

The Butterfly Centre [30]

Royal Parade, Eastbourne, East Sussex, BN22 7AQ
(On the sea side of the promenade at the eastern end)
Tel: 0323 645522
Proprietor: Barbara Goodall

Open: Every day from Palm Sunday to the end of October, and on weekends and Bank Holidays from 10.00 to 5.00

Admission Fees: £2.00 adults, £1.00 children between 5 and 16 years, £1.40 OAPs. Party rates on application

Additional Costs: There is a 'pay and display' car park next door

Catering: Refreshments available nearby

Facilities for Children: Ideal for children of all ages

Facilities for the Disabled: There is wide access for wheelchairs

Restrictions: No dogs are allowed except for guide dogs. Unaccompanied children are admitted at the discretion of the management

This is a walk-through jungle, filled with around 500 free-flying butterflies and moths at the height of the season. One can watch everything from egg-laying through to the emergence of the adult insect from the pupal case, provided you are patient and lucky. School parties are very welcome, and guided tours can be arranged provided they are booked in advance. There is an extraordinarily useful education pack available which contains all sorts of information — not just about butterflies, but about how they fit into the environment.

Drusilla's Park [31]

Alfriston, East Sussex, BN26 5QS
(Between Brighton and Eastbourne, off the A27 1 mile
(1 ½ km) north of Alfriston)
Tel: 0323 870234
Proprietor: Michael Ann and Family

Open: Every day from 10.30 to 5.00, or dusk in winter

Admission Fees: £2.99 adults and children. £2.00 OAPs. Party rates for groups of 15 or over: £2.00. These prices are for admission to the zoo, the railway ride, and an adventure playland

Additional Costs: Car parking costs 50p. A sticker allows free parking in future

Catering: There is a restaurant and function rooms, and a fast-food area

Facilities for Children: Children's meals are available, and high chairs. There are also baby changing facilities

Facilities for the Disabled: Wheelchairs may be borrowed, and there are toilets for the disabled. There are no steps anywhere

Restrictions: Dogs are not allowed in the zoo or in Playland. Elsewhere they must be kept on leads. Feeding the animals is not permitted

This collection is a child's first zoo. It specialises in small animals. Ring Tailed Lemurs, Cotton Top Tamarins, Goeldi's Monkeys, Humboldt's Penguins, Cereopsis Geese and other, more common species breed here regularly. The zoo won an award in 1987 for 'The Best New Zoo Exhibit in Britain' for the beaver colony. No wire netting separates people from other animals. All the enclosures are either open, or glass fronted. Education plays an important part here and the department is regarded as in the top eight in the country for its work. There is a school room and a film theatre. They also produce a junior education magazine.

Living World [32]

Seven Sisters Country Park, Exceat, Seaford, East Sussex, BN25 4AD
(On the A259, 6 miles (10 km) west of Eastbourne, and 2 miles (3 km) east of Seaford)
Tel: 0323 870100
Proprietors: David and Janice Rushen

Open: From Easter until 1 November Living World is open every day. Thereafter at weekends, half terms and school holidays only

Admission Fees: (1989) £1.70 adults, £1.00 children under 16 years, £1.00 OAPs. Groups of twenty or over can claim a 10% discount

Additional Costs: None

Catering: There is an ice cream stall

Facilities for Children: There are steps up in front of higher exhibits so that small children can see them properly

Facilities for the Disabled: There are ramps where necessary. Wheelchairs are available, and there is a toilet for the disabled

Restrictions: None

Although Living World calls itself an Invertebrate Zoo, and although it is true that most of the animals are invertebrates, there are also fish to be seen. One can conveniently divide the animals into two groups: the insects and arachnids on the one hand, and marine life on the other. One can enjoy watching butterflies, Honey Bees and Giant Land Snails as well as fish and aquatic invertebrates. There is in addition a display of minerals lit by ultra violet light which reveals the most astonishing colours. On top of that there are 700 acres (283 ha) of country park containing downland, forest, river and estuary, which visitors can explore. Teachers can obtain work packs, and there are extensive educational panels of text and photographs.

Sewerby Park Zoo [33]

Sewerby Hall, Bridlington, East Yorkshire, YO15 3JH
(In Sewerby village, 2 miles (3 km) north east of
Bridlington)
Tel: 0262 673769
Proprietor: East Yorkshire Borough Council

Open: Every day from 8.00 to dusk

Admission Fees: £1.00 adults, 50p children under 14 years. These prices are
from 9.00 to 5.00 between the Spring Bank Holiday and the end of
September. The rest of the year, and in the evenings, the cost is 20p. These
prices are for 1988

Additional Costs: Car parking costs 50p for 4 hours

Catering: There is a cafe, a bar, and an ice cream stall during the peak
season only

Facilities for Children: None

Facilities for the Disabled: There is easy access, and toilet facilities are
available

Restrictions: No dogs are allowed in the zoo, and there are restrictions on
feeding certain animals

This is a small, strange, but interesting place to visit. It sees itself as
mainly a children's zoo, and with delightful frankness they tell me that
though they have bred no rare species, the remainder of the animals are
embarrassingly fertile! Within the zoo itself one finds Fantail Pigeons,
waterfowl, flamingoes and peafowl. Besides the well-stocked aviaries
there are also Llamas, monkeys, Coatis, penguins, goats and rabbits.
Elsewhere in the grounds there are also deer, wallabies and ponies. A
lecture room is available if it is booked in advance, and there are guided
tours by members of the keeping staff.

The house and gardens are full of other attractions such as a
playground, gardens, an orchid house, a museum and an art gallery, and
various outdoor games including boules (and bowls).

Colchester Zoological Gardens
[34]

**Stanway Hall, Maldon Road, Colchester, Essex,
CO3 5SL**
(Take the A604 Cambridge exit from the A12, and follow
the signs along the Maldon Road. The zoo can also be
reached by bus from Colchester)
Tel: 0206 330253
Proprietor: Colchester Zoo Ltd

Open: Every day except Christmas Day from 9.30 to 5.30 (or dusk in winter)

Admission Fees: £2.70 adults, £1.30 children (under 14 years), £2.10 OAPs.
Party rates for twenty or more: £2.20 adults, £1.10 children, £1.80 OAPs.
School party rates: £1.10 for everyone, though one teacher is admitted free
with every ten children. The zoo makes the point that these figures are for
1988

Additional Costs: Safari Express: 50p adults, 30p children

Catering: There is a cafeteria, and kiosks that serve ice cream, food and hot
drinks

Facilities for Children: Children's meals are available, and there is an
adventure playground and an amusement arcade

Facilities for the Disabled: The natural hilly terrain makes some areas
difficult for wheelchairs. Toilets for the disabled are available

Restrictions: No dogs, except in the car park, where they must be kept on a
lead. Animals may only be fed in the Familiar Friends Patting Area

Colchester Zoo is in a lovely setting with Stanway Hall at its centre, and
an old ruined church within the grounds. It has much improved in recent
years, and new buildings are going up all the time. The range of animals
is large, and include Zeedonks which, if nothing else, attract publicity.
There is an education officer and a lecture room, and the zoo has won
an award for breeding Black Spider Monkeys. It houses the only
breeding group of Black Mangabeys in the country. There are falconry
displays and sealion shows.

Mole Hall Wildlife Park [35]

**Widdington, Saffron Walden, Essex,
CB11 3SS**
(2 miles (3 km) off the B1383 — the old
A11 — just south of Newport, Essex)
Tel: 0799 40400
Proprietors: The Johnstone Family

Open: Every day except Christmas Day from 10.30 to 6.00 (or dusk in winter). The Butterfly House is open from mid-March to 31 October

Admission Fees: £2.50 adults, £1.50 children under 16 years (under 3s are free), £1.50 OAPs. Party rates, £2.00 adults, £1.25 children, and a flat £1.25 where children predominate

Additional Costs: None

Catering: There is a cafeteria, but from 1 November to mid-March it is open only on Sundays

Facilities for Children: Pets corner and play area with seesaws and other amusements

Facilities for the Disabled: None, though wheelchairs can go anywhere except for the Field Walk and the Butterfly House

Restrictions: Dogs are allowed only in the 2-acre (1-ha) grass car park

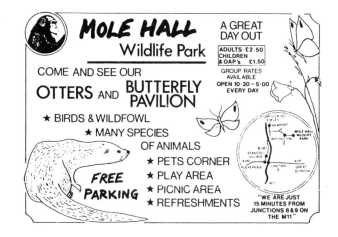

This is a small, but good, private collection of mammals and birds, together with a Butterfly House. There are three species of otter, an animal in which the collection specialises. You can see the only breeding group of Canadian Otters in the country. You can also see primates, deer, Servals, pigs and much else. Illustrated lectures on butterflies or on otters can be booked for a fee. Gardens, attached to the fully moated Manor House, are well worth looking at, though the house itself is not open to the public.

Wellgate Community Farm [36]

Collier Road Row, Romford, Essex, RM5 3NX
(Opposite the Oaks Centre and in front of Collier Row Football Club,
off the A1112)
Tel: 01 599 0415
Proprietor: The Wellgate Farm Charitable Trust

Open: Every day between 9.30 and 3.30 on weekdays, and between 9.00
and 12.00 at weekends, or at other times by appointment

Admission Fees: None, though donations are welcome. Any individual,
family or group can become members of the Trust

Additional Costs: None

Catering: There is a shop that will sell teas, ice creams, sweets and other
snacks. It is opened for groups that have booked in advance

Facilities for Children: Children are welcome to become involved where
possible

Facilities for the Disabled: Nearly everything is accessible to wheelchairs

Restrictions: No dogs are allowed. Check with staff about the feeding of the
animals

This is a small, compact, working city farm where one can meet a
variety of animals and discover what their lives are like on a properly
run farm. This farm has the only herd of British Lop Pigs in Essex,
though the animals are often at their other home in a school at Chigwell.
There is also a flock of Herdwick Sheep. A wild flower area is being
developed, and visitors can buy produce from the farm according to the
season, and goats' milk yoghurt. Try it if you haven't done before, and
you'll never want another pot of supermarket rubbish in your life. There
is a project room, and simple quizzes and activities are available for
groups.

Birdland and Windrush Trout Farm [37]

Rissington Road, Bourton on the Water, Cheltenham, Gloucestershire, GL54 2BN
(Follow the River Windrush downstream from the centre of the village for 550 yards (500 m))
Tel: 0451 20689
Proprietor: Aviculture Ltd

Open: Every day from 10.30 till 5.30, or dusk in winter

Admission Fees: £1.50 adults, £1.00 children under 14, and OAPs. Parties receive a 10% discount. These are 1988 figures and fees will go up

Additional Costs: None, but there are no car parking facilities

Catering: Ice cream and sweets may be bought, and there is a shop at the Trout Farm

Facilities for Children: None

Facilities for the Disabled: None

Restrictions: None

Birdland is a beautiful bird collection set in the middle of a beautiful village in the Cotswolds. It was one of the very first and today it has an astounding number of species in a very small area. The place is packed with birds in delightful settings or at liberty. Many species have been bred at Birdland and there are some lovely walk-through aviaries for smaller species. You will find the most extraordinary birds at liberty in this collection, and I can guarantee that if you like birds you will love this place.

The Falconry Centre [38]

Newent, Gloucestershire, GL18 1JJ
(1½ miles (2½ km) from the centre of Newent, off the B4221)
Tel: 0531 820286
Proprietors: Joe and Jemima Parry-Jones

Open: The Centre is closed during December and January. From February to May, and from September to November it is open every day except Tuesday. During June, July and August it is open every day. Opening times are 10.30 to 5.30, or dusk in winter

Admission Fees: £2.50 adults, £1.75 children under 16 years. Enquire about party rates for groups of 18 or more

Additional Costs: None

Catering: There is a cafeteria, and an ice cream stall in the gift shop

Facilities for Children: None, apart from an adventure playground

Facilities for the Disabled: The paths are all of flat gravel with ramps where necessary. Toilets are provided for the disabled

Restrictions: No dogs allowed

The Falconry Centre has the largest collection of birds of prey in the Western world; there are over 200 birds. They are constantly breeding birds of prey at Newent, some of which are now being returned to the wild to replenish hard-pressed wild stocks. Conservation and education are regarded as most important, and an education pack is available, and talks are frequently given to schools. In case you think that all there is to be seen is a lot of bored falcons sitting in rows, let me say that is not the case. The high spots of any visit are the displays of falconry when birds are flown at artificial lures. Goldie, the famous London Zoo Golden Eagle now lives at Newent, and there are also a few other birds, such as parrots, to be seen. A day not to be missed.

The Wildfowl Trust [39]

Slimbridge, Gloucestershire, GL2 7BT
(The reserve may be reached from the M5 — Junctions 13 and 14 — and lies 2 miles (3 km) off the A38 through the village of Slimbridge)
Tel: 045 389333
Proprietor: The Wildfowl Trust

Open: Every day except Christmas Eve and Christmas Day from 9.30 to 5.00, or to 4.00 in winter

Admission Fees: (1988) £2.80 adults, £1.30 children between 4 and 16 years, £2.00 OAPs. The party rate for groups of 20 or more is £2.00. Enquire about special rates for schools

Additional Costs: Parking and the tropical house are free, but donations are appreciated

Catering: There is a restaurant, a confectionary counter, and an ice cream kiosk in the car park

Facilities for Children: There are nature trails, a mother's nursing room, sound effects, sit-on wildfowl models, and children may feed the birds

Facilities for the Disabled: There are wheelchairs available and ramps where necessary. In addition there are hides that will take wheelchairs, a special parking area, a Braille trail with cassettes and players, and a guide-dog compound. There is a suitable toilet, and talks, tactile exhibits and guided tours by arrangement

Restrictions: Dogs are not permitted in the reserve

As a day out for someone who is interested in waterfowl you cannot do better than visit Slimbridge, nor just because there are plenty of them there, but because of the care and facilities that are to be found. And if you do get bored with ducks and geese, there is the tropical house to enjoy, full of hummingbirds, sunbirds and other exotic delights. Much serious scientific work goes on at Slimbridge, but even the most casual visitor will surely know the conservation achievements of this collection, the most notable of which must surely be the hauling back from the brink of extinction of the Hawaiian Goose. These are now commonplace in waterfowl collections, but that was not so only a short time ago. There are about 180 different species of waterfowl in the grounds, and if you thought all ducks were brown, look again — they come in just about every colour of the rainbow. There are 800 acres (324 ha) to enjoy, and in addition to the ducks, geese and swans there are the flamingoes. Every species of flamingo in the world has bred here. If you find yourself moved or excited by all the birds, and I challenge you not to be, why not join the Adopt a Duck scheme. Teachers will discover that the education facilities are comprehensive, and even residential courses can be arranged.

Cannon Aquarium and Vivarium [40]

The Manchester Museum, The University, Oxford Road, Manchester, M13 9PL
Tel: 061 275 2000
Proprietors: Alan Warhurst and David Wareham

Open: Every day except Sunday, Christmas Day, Boxing Day, Good Friday, May Day and New Year's Day from 10.00 to 5.00

Admission Fees: None

Catering: Visitors may get refreshments in the university refectory

Facilities for Children: None

Facilities for the Disabled: Ramps and lifts are available for the disabled

Restrictions: No dogs are admitted, neither are children under 14 if they are unaccompanied by an adult. Feeding of the animals is forbidden

This is a fascinating collection of coldwater and tropical freshwater fish, snakes, lizards, turtles, amphibians and crocodiles. In 1988 they bred Black Rat Snakes, Yellow Rat Snakes, Banded Water Snakes, Slow Worms, Leopard Geckoes, Corn Snakes and Blue Tongued Skinks. All the animals are kept in roomy enclosures under simulated natural conditions. Full educational facilities are available such as talks, films, leaflets and worksheets. Phone Richard Porter and ask for details. Elsewhere within the museum one can see collections of coins, archery equipment, Egyptology, botany, zoology, geology, minerals, dinosaurs and much else.

/ # The Hawk Conservancy [41]

Weyhill, Andover, Hampshire, SP11 8DY
(Just off the A303, 4 miles (6½ km) west of Andover)
Tel: 0264 772252
Proprietor: The Hawk Conservancy is run by a family company

Open: Every day from 1 March to the last Sunday in October from 10.30 until 5.00 in the summer, and in the spring and autumn the last visitors are admitted at 4.00

Admission Fees: (1988) £2.00 adults, £1.25 children between 3 and 15 years, £1.60 OAPs. Parties of 20 and over are admitted for 10% less when they book in advance

Additional Costs: None

Catering: There is a restaurant

Facilities for Children: None

Facilities for the Disabled: The site is pretty flat, though it is of grass. Plans for toilets for the disabled are expected to go ahead in the near future

Restrictions: No dogs are allowed, though they may be left in cars in the car park, and no unaccompanied children may enter

Though a visitor will see other birds around, this collection is about birds of prey. Though there are falconry displays daily, the organisation does not promote falconry nor sell birds. It is primarily interested in breeding birds of prey. Many are then released in the wild, or exchanged with other, similar collections. Another aspect of their work is the care of injured raptors. Many such casualties are brought in each year, as are apparently abandoned chicks. Introductory talks are given to school groups, and there are some interesting worksheets for children to complete. Worksheet No. 2 contains some beautiful line drawings of birds of prey by Pam Mullins.

The New Forest Butterfly Farm [42]

Longdown, Ashurst, Southampton, SO4 4UH
(Just off the A35 between Totton and Lyndhurst)
Tel: 042129 2166
Proprietor: Mrs A.V. Hudson Davies

Open: Every day between Easter and the end of October from 10.00 to 5.00

Admission Fees: (1988) £2.50 adults, £1.50 children under 14 years, £2.20 OAPs. Party rates: £2.15 adults, £1.30 children, £1.90 OAPs

Additional Costs: Woodland Wagon rides £1.30 adults, £1.00 children, £1.30 OAPs

Catering: There is a cafeteria

Facilities for Children: Children's meals are available, and there is an adventure playground

Facilities for the Disabled: There are ramps where necessary, and a toilet for the disabled

Restrictions: No dogs are allowed, and neither are unaccompanied children

This is said to be the first butterfly farm of its kind to open in Britain. There has been considerable success in breeding many exotic species using British foodplants. From an educational point of view, talks and guided tours are given to all school parties.

Marwell Zoological Park [43]

Colden Common, Winchester, Hampshire, SO21 1JH
(Situated on the B2177, Winchester to Bishop's Waltham road, ¼ mile (400 m) past Fisher's Pond)
Tel: 0962 74406 for inquiries about prices or 0962 74407 for other queries
Proprietor: Marwell Preservation Trust Ltd

Open: Every day from 10.00 to 6.00

Admission Fees: £3.20 adults, £2.00 children between 3 and 14 years, £2.70 OAPs. Party rates (minimum 20) are £2.70 (£2.20 OAPs)

Additional Costs: Parking is free, but cars entering the park cost £3.00 unless they have a disabled sticker. Train rides are 50p single and 80p return

Catering: There is a licensed restaurant, a fast-food cafe and a sweet shop. There are also three kiosks

Facilities for Children: There are pushchairs available at the gate, and children's portions in the restaurant

Facilities for the Disabled: There are ramps for access where necessary and wheelchairs may be borrowed at the gate. Suitable toilets are provided

Restrictions: No dogs or other pets are allowed; they can be left in kennels. Children must be accompanied by an adult

Marwell Zoo is a highly respected organisation in the world of animal people. Not only is a visit a splendid way to spend a day, but it is also a way of learning the tremendous strides that are being made in conservation these days in the face of ever increasing pressure. Marwell contributes to the re-introduction of Scimitar-horned Oryx to Tunisia, Golden Lion Tamarins in Brazil, pheasant eggs to Pakistan and Nepal via the World Pheasant Association, and Père David's Deer to China. Many rare species of animal are bred here and you can see the only breeding group of Nyala antelope in Britain. As you may imagine, there is a good educational programme and superb facilities during term time, and animal handling sessions during the holidays.

Paultons Park [44]

Ower, Romsey, Hampshire, SO51 6AL
(Just off Junction 2 of the M27)
Tel: 0703 814442
Proprietor: Paultons Park Ltd

Open: Every day from March to October between 10.00 and 6.30

Admission Fees: (1988) £3.00 adults, £2.50 children between 3 and 14 years, £2.50 OAPs. Party rates for groups of 20 or more: £2.70 adults, £2.20 children and OAPs

Additional Costs: Go karts £1.00 per ride, coin-operated fun activities

Catering: There is a restaurant, burger bars, ice cream kiosks and tea rooms. There is also a tuck shop

Facilities for Children: There are special children's menus and birthday parties. The park has many facilities for children including Kids Kingdom, a 3-acre (1¼-ha) site full of play structures. There is a Rabbit Ride, trampolines, bouncy castle, coin-operated boats and cars, aqua bugs, the Magic Forest, Captain Blood's Cavern and lots more

Facilities for the Disabled: Wheelchairs are available, all paths are flat and mainly tarmaced, and there are toilets for the disabled

Restrictions: No dogs are allowed, and children must be supervised by a responsible adult

The 8 acres (3¼ ha) of grounds in which this astonishing collection is housed, were originally landscaped by Capability Brown. The bird collection contains a wide variety of exotic and interesting species from Emus to mynahs. There is an extensive collection of wildfowl as well. In addition there are quite a few mammals living here. There are shaggy Highland Cattle, king-sized-guinea-pig-like Capybara, deer, Llamas, goats and Shetland Ponies. Work is done in conjunction with other zoological collections to breed endangered species of birds such as Snowy Owls, Roseate Cockatoos and wildfowl. Glass-fronted tropical aviaries allow visitors an excellent view of birds without disturbing them. There is a lecture room, and various appropriate educational publications. There is a wealth of native wildlife in the grounds. There are dozens of other attractions from water mills to museums. Paultons Park makes a great day out for everyone.

Willersmill Fish Farm and Wild Animal Sanctuary [45]

**Station Road, Shepreth, Royston,
Hertfordshire, SG8 6PZ**
(Next door to Shepreth railway station)
Tel: 0763 61832
Proprietor: Terry Willers

Open: Every day from 15 March to 31 October from 10.30 to 6.00, and at weekends only for the rest of the year from 10.30 to dusk

Admission Fees: £2.50 adults, £1.25 children under 16 years, £1.75 OAPs. Party rates for groups of not less than 14: 10% discount if you book in advance and pay when you arrive, or 20% discount if you book and pay in advance

Additional Costs: Pony rides are 50p

Catering: There is a cafeteria and an ice cream stall

Facilities for Children: None

Facilities for the Disabled: None

Restrictions: The fish, ponies, goats, sheep and ducks may only be fed on food purchased on the premises for 15p a bag

This is a funny little collection that is more interesting than it sounds. The sanctuary is somewhere for unwanted or injured animals to live in safety. They come as unwanted pets or from research centres that would otherwise kill them at the end of experimentation, or they are road casualties, and some even turn up all by themselves. Most of them have the run of the place and could leave if they wished, but some are kept in captive conditions because of their special requirements. It would be wrong to think that they are all hedgehogs or bunnies, however, for there are marmosets, terrapins, Coatis, snakes, and much else. There is also a fish farm where the carp will feed from your fingers. A number of ornamental varieties of fish are bred here, and visitors can buy specimens for their own collections.

Questionnaires are available to teachers, and there is a wild animal hospital on the premises where newly arrived animals are cared for.

Blean Bird Park [46]

Honey Hill, Blean, Canterbury, Kent, CT2 9JP
(Midway between Canterbury and Whitstable on the A290)
Tel: 0227 471666
Proprietor: N.P. Tabony

Open: Every day from 1 March to 30 November from 10.00 to 6.00

Admission Fees: £2.00 adults, £1.25 children under 15 years, £1.50 OAPs.
Party rates for groups of 20 or over can claim a 10% discount on these figures

Additional Costs: None

Catering: There is a cafeteria

Facilities for Children: There is a Pets Corner and an adventure playground

Facilities for the Disabled: There are ramps, and toilets for the disabled

Restrictions: No dogs are allowed

This is a collection for the parrot enthusiast. It is true that there are a few other birds in the park, but the whole point of the operation is to keep and breed parrots. This is the largest collection of these birds that is open to the public. There has been considerable success in breeding most species of the large macaws and cockatoos as well as plenty of smaller birds including owls and Kestrels. From an educational point of view there is a fact sheet available and a delightful woodland walk. It is often forgotten that many species of parrots are becoming endangered these days and collections like this one are vital if we are not to lose some of them. Captive bred birds also mean that the drain on wild-caught parrots can be reduced.

Brambles English Wildlife Park [47]

Wealden Forest, Herne Common, Canterbury, Kent, CT6 7LQ
(Halfway between Herne Bay and Canterbury on the A291)
Tel: 0227 712379
Proprietor: Brambles English Wildlife Park is run by a staff co-operative

Open: Every day from Easter to October between 10.00 and 5.00

Admission Fees: £1.60 adults, 80p children, £1.25 OAPs

Additional Costs: None

Catering: Snacks are available

Facilities for Children: Children's snacks can be obtained, there is an under-fives play area, and a baby changing room

Facilities for the Disabled: There is a ramp to the toilets, and there are no other steps

Restrictions: No dogs are allowed, nor are unaccompanied children, and, so they tell me, only 'nice and cheerful people' will be admitted!

Brambles is set in 20 acres (8 ha) of natural woodland. The visitor can follow the nature trail to see Fallow and Sika Deer, owls and foxes. Children will love feeding the farm animals with bags of food which can be bought for 20p. There is an enclosed garden with laid-out ponds full of amphibians and fish. There is a rabbit world, a very large duckpond, and Scottish Wildcats. There has been considerable success breeding from injured wildlife that has been brought in, and the young have been released into the wild. This is said to be the only frog and toad farm in the country which releases these animals into the wild. Educational worksheets are available on request.

The Butterfly Centre [48]

Macfarlanes Nurseries, Swingfield, Dover, Kent
(On the A260 Canterbury to Folkestone road, 5 miles (8 km) from
the latter and 12 miles (19 km) from Canterbury)
Tel: 0303 83244
Proprietors: J.M. Hill and F.L. Macfarlane

Open: Every day from 1 April to 30 September from 10.00 to 5.00

Admission Fees: £1.70 adults, £1.05 children, £1.15 OAPs, £4.75 for a
family of four. There are special rates for coaches

Additional Costs: None

Catering: There is a cafe that serves light refreshments and ice cream

Facilities for Children: None

Facilities for the Disabled: There is easy access for wheelchairs

Restrictions: No dogs are allowed

This is a typically interesting butterfly centre where one can walk
through a jungle filled with tropical plants and watch numbers of exotic
butterflies flying free. Worksheets, brief talks and guided tours can be
arranged for schools or other groups with an educational reason for the
visit. There is a garden centre to visit after your enthusiasm has been
roused by seeing the plants in the tropical house. Incidentally, if you
feel like breeding butterflies yourself, don't buy foodplants from a
nursery or garden centre and expect to use them straight away. Such
plants have been treated with insecticides which are most effective for
killing caterpillars!

Howletts Zoo Park [49]

Bekesbourne, Canterbury, Kent, CT4 5EL
(3 miles (5 km) south of Canterbury, signposted from
the A2)
Tel: 0227 721286
Proprietor: John Aspinall

Open: Every day except Christmas Day from 10.00 to 5.00, or one hour
before dusk in winter

Admission Fees: (1987) £3.50 adults, £2.50 children between 4 and 14
years, £2.50 OAPs. Party rates for groups of 20 or more: £3.00 adults, £2.00
children

Additional Costs: None

Catering: There is a licensed cafeteria and an ice cream kiosk, refreshment
kiosks, and a tea room

Facilities for Children: Children's meals are available

Facilities for the Disabled: There are ramps where necessary, and toilets for
the disabled

Restrictions: No dogs are allowed, and feeding the animals is forbidden

This, together with its sister, Port Lympne Zoo Park, is one of my
favourite collections. Old zoo images die hard, and let's face it, there
have been some disgusting zoos in this country. However, despite
objections from some quarters, there is no doubt that when an animal
has all its physical and psychological needs catered for, it is infinitely
better off in captivity than in the wild. Only when you have observed
animals in the forests of South America, the grasslands of Africa, or the
amazing jungles of South East Asia, do you realise that this is so. And
you will certainly not find many captive animals kept as well as they are
here.

The collection contains all sorts of goodies such as gorillas, Tigers,
Honey Badgers, Clouded Leopards, Snow Leopards, African Elephants,
Dhole, lynxes and much else. Where else would you see Dhole, or a
group of 35 Lowland Gorillas. This latter is the largest in the world.
There is also the only breeding group of African elephants in Britain,
and if that doesn't sound too impressive, look up what has been written

about breeding elephants in captivity. There are heaps of cats and primates, and a very few birds. Education plays an important part here, and interested teachers should ask about details. This is not the place to talk at length about Sumatran Rhinos and gorillas, but when you have time, look up Howletts' involvement with the conservation of these two species.

Leeds Castle [50]

Maidstone, Kent, ME17 1PL
(4 miles (6½ km) east of Maidstone at the junction of the A20 and M20, just off the B2163)
Tel: 0622 65400
Proprietor: Leeds Castle Foundation

Open: Every day from 1 April to 31 October from 11.00 till the last admission at 5.00. Between November and March it is open between 12.00 and 4.00 on Saturdays and Sundays, and it is closed on 1 July and 4 November prior to special events

Admission Fees: £4.80 adults, £3.30 children under 15 years, £3.80 OAPs and students, £14.50 family ticket. Party rates (minimum number is 20): £3.80 adults, £2.80 children, £3.30 OAPs and students

Additional Costs: None

Catering: The Fairfax Hall — a restored 17th-century tithe barn — is a licensed restaurant, offering a good choice of hot or cold dishes. The 'Loose Box' supplies hot and cold drinks, rolls and gateaux, and there are barbecues in Fairfax courtyard when the weather is fine

Facilities for Children: There is a changing room for babies

Facilities for the Disabled: There is a car park for the disabled, a wheelchair lift inside the castle, ramps at strategic positions in the castle and grounds, and toilets for the disabled

Restrictions: No dogs or radios are allowed; children should be kept under gentle supervision, and no pushchairs must be taken into the castle

Leeds Castle is a castle, with a whole heap of fascinating things for the visitor to see and do, but from the point of view of this book, the most interesting is the collection of birds. It was Lady Baillie, who owned the castle until her death in 1974, who started keeping birds, and in time became famous for her parrots, mostly Australian species, and her extensive collection of waterfowl. There are other birds as well — 48 aviaries of them — many being rare and endangered species from around the world. School parties and other educational groups are welcomed and a guided tour can be provided free of charge. A children's Activity Book is available at 50p. Leeds Castle has been called 'The loveliest castle in the world', and it is set in 500 acres (200 ha) of magnificent parkland and gardens which include the Culpeper Garden, a secret grotto, a vineyard and a woodland garden. There is also a dog-collar museum which contains a unique collection of collars dating from medieval times.

Port Lympne Zoo Park [51]

Port Lympne, Lympne, Hythe, Kent, CT21 4PD
(Just off the A20 between Ashford and Folkestone. Leave
the M20 at Junction 11 and head for Lympne)
Tel: 0303 264646
Proprietor: John Aspinall

Open: Every day except Christmas Day from 10.00 to 5.00, or one hour
before dusk in winter

Admission Fees: (1987) £3.50 adults, £2.50 children between the ages of 4
and 14 years, £2.50 OAPs. Party rates for groups of 20 or more: £3.00 adults,
£2.00 children

Additional Costs: There are safari trailer journeys through various animal
enclosures. It is advisable to book these

Catering: There are a licensed cafeteria, ice cream kiosks, barbecue kiosks
and refreshment kiosks

Facilities for Children: Children's meals are available, and there are high
chairs in the cafeteria

Facilities for the Disabled: Only parts of the zoo park are suitable for
wheelchairs. There are toilets for the disabled

Restrictions: No dogs are allowed, and no feeding of the animals

This zoo and its sister collection, Howletts, is one for which I have
much affection. They have come in for criticism in the past that I
consider completely unwarranted. The animals in both of them contain
some desperately endangered species, and their breeding record is
impressive. They have bred Tigers, Black Rhinos, Snow Leopards,
Przewalski's Horses, Barasingha, Barbary Lions, Colobus Monkeys and
much else. Only at this zoo can you see a pair of Sumatran Rhinos — at
least in the western world — and if you have not seen these animals
you ought to, as they are quite delightful. They also have here the only
breeding group of Barbary Lions in Britain, and the second largest herd
of Przewalski's Horses in the world, 48 of them. I could go on for ever,
but go and see the place yourself. There are plenty of educational
facilities for teachers. If you are interested in horticulture or botany, the
gardens will blow your mind. They are quite magnificent, and the
mansion is also well worth a visit. Not only is it of historical interest,
but it contains fascinating features such as the Tent Room. While you
are in the mansion, don't miss the natural history murals.

Wingham Bird Park [52]

Wingham, Canterbury, Kent, CT3 1JL
(1 mile (1½ km) from Wingham on the A257 towards Sandwich)
Tel: 0227 720836
Proprietor: Mosaad Saad Gabr

Open: Every day except Christmas Day from 10.00 to 6.00

Admission Fees: £2.00 adults, £1.00 children, £1.00 OAPs, £5.00 family
ticket for two adults and two children. Disabled visitors are admitted free.
Party rate for groups of 20 or more may deduct 15% from these prices

Additional Costs: None

Catering: There is a tea room

Facilities for Children: There are ramps where necessary for pushchairs

Facilities for the Disabled: There are ramps where necessary for
wheelchairs

Restrictions: No dogs are allowed

This is a private collection of interesting and colourful birds, many
housed in large walk-through aviaries. There is also a pet shop, a
children's play area and 30 acres (12 ha) of soft fruit which is sold to
visitors on a Pick-Your-Own basis.

WINGHAM BIRD PARK

WINGHAM,
CANTERBURY

For a wonderful day out for the whole family,
visit Wingham Bird Park at Wingham near
Canterbury. You can see birds of many species,
all in large flights and beautiful surroundings.
Picnic area, tea room, gift and pet shops and
free parking.

10p OFF
The voucher entitles the holder to 10p reduction on the normal admission charges of
£2.00 adult, £1.00 children and OAP. Open every day (except Christmas Day)
10am to 6pm. Wingham Bird Park, Wingham, Canterbury, Kent. (On the A257
between Wingham and Sandwich) Tel: (0227) 720836.

N.Z. 89

Bolton Aquarium [53]

**Bolton Museum and Art Gallery, Le Mans Crescent, Bolton,
BL1 1SE**
(In the town centre, the aquarium is to be found in the basement of
the Central Museum and Library, opposite the Octagon Theatre)
Tel: 0204 22311 extension 2200
Proprietor: Bolton Metropolitan Borough

Open: Every Monday, Tuesday, Thursday and Friday from 10.00 to 5.30, and
every Saturday from 10.00 to 5.00

Admission Fees: None

Additional Costs: None

Catering: There is a cafeteria

Facilities for Children: None

Facilities for the Disabled: By arrangement only

Restrictions: No dogs are admitted except for guide dogs, and no smoking

Bolton Aquarium is a fascinating little collection. There are 23 tanks,
one being the home to some marine fish, one housing Black Rat Snakes
which have bred, and the remainder being divided between displays of
temperate freshwater and tropical freshwater species of fish. There is a
good collection of catfish including the Red Tailed, the Tiger Shovel
Nosed and the European Wel's Catfish. There are also some rare
livebearers, notably *Chapalichthys pardalus* and *Ilyodon xantusi*, names
which will be of interest to fishkeepers. There is also a good display of
Rift Valley Cichlids which are especially interesting. There are various
species of these living in a few African lakes. Because of their beauty
they have been over collected for the tropical fish trade, and then to
make matters worse someone introduced Nile Perch into the waters
some years ago, and they started to eat what was left of the original
inhabitants. Consequently, some of them are now endangered so there
is an international scheme to breed these animals, and Bolton is taking
part. It will not be possible to reintroduce these fish into their original
lakes because the Nile Perch are still there, but at least we won't lose
them. Extinction is for ever. For teachers who would like to follow this
fascinating story further, the museum's education service can arrange
school visits.

Haigh Miniature Zoo [54]

Haigh Country Park, Aspull, Wigan
(1 mile (1½ km) from the B5239)
Tel: 0942 831261
Proprietor: Wigan Borough Department of Leisure

Open: Between Easter and October from 10.00 to 5.30

Admission Fees: £1.20 adults, 60p children over 4 years. Enquire about party rates

Additional Costs: None stated

Catering: There is a cafeteria, and another should be opening in 1989

Facilities for Children: Children's meals are available, and there is a play area

Facilities for the Disabled: Wheelchairs are available, and there are ramps where necessary

Restrictions: No dogs are allowed, and no feeding of the animals

This is a small collection comprising a variety of exotic animals including zebras, lynx, baboons and birds. Educational leaflets are available. This collection is perhaps not worth a visit on its own, but in the grounds of the country park there is much to see and do, from a model village to gardens, crazy golf course and a model boat lake.

The Wildfowl Trust [55]

Martin Mere, Burscough, Ormskirk, Lancashire, L40 0TA
(From the M6 take the A5209 to Burscough Bridge. The reserve lies
2 miles (3 km) from Burscough)
Tel: 0704 895181
Proprietor: The Wildfowl Trust

Open: Every day except Christmas Eve and Christmas Day from 9.30 to 5.30
in summer and 4.00 in winter

Admission Fees: (1988) £2.20 adults, £1.10 children between 4 and 16
years, £1.40 OAPs. Party rate for groups of 20 and over: £1.80. Enquire
about special rates for school parties

Additional Costs: None

Catering: There is a licensed coffee shop serving light refreshments

Facilities for Children: There are play areas, easy paths for pushchairs,
nature trails, and the children can feed the birds

Facilities for the Disabled: There are free wheelchairs, toilet facilities,
special parking areas, a Braille trail, tactile exhibits, and free loan of cassettes
and players

Restrictions: No dogs are allowed into the reserve

Once the largest lake in Lancashire, Martin Mere is now a marshland
reserve for vast numbers of waterfowl. The gardens feature 1500
ducks, geese and swans from all over the world together with flocks of
flamingoes bred by the Wildfowl Trust. Spacious hides allow for
marvellous views of the 300-acre (121-ha) site. Thousands of Pink
Footed Geese and an ever growing number of Bewick's and Whooper
Swans, as well as a host of ducks and waders, join the residents in
winter. Talks, films and guided tours can be arranged, and there is a
lecture and film theatre as well as two classrooms. Worksheets are
available for educational purposes.

The Animal Gardens [56]

North End, Mablethorpe, Lincolnshire, LN12 1QG
(At the north end of Mablethorpe, 1½ miles (2½ km) from
the main 'Pullover' in the town centre)
Tel: 0521 73346
Proprietor: The King Family

Open: Every day from Easter to October from 10.00 to 6.00 or one hour
before dusk

Admission Fees: £1.50 adults, 75p children under 15 years, £1.00 OAPs.
Enquire about party rates

Additional Costs: None. Full refund given on parking ticket

Catering: There is a tea room

Facilities for Children: None, apart from a play area

Facilities for the Disabled: 90% of the gardens are accessible to the
disabled

Restrictions: No dogs and no unaccompanied children

The Animal Gardens opened in 1973 when the present curator's parents
wanted to establish a breeding centre for wild animals and at the same
time to allow visitors to learn about the problems the animals have of
surviving. Two acres (¾ ha) of delightful gardens today provide the
setting for over 200 animals. The collection is surprisingly comprehensive for a small collection, and all the animals are birds and mammals. A
large part of the zoo's work consists of caring for oiled, orphaned or
injured birds and seals, which are released back into the wild wherever
possible. There have been notable successes with the breeding of
Salmon Crested Cockatoos, Sulphur Crested Cockatoos and other
parrots, as well as mynahs, Racoons, Arctic Foxes, porcupines, and
much else.

Long Sutton Butterfly Park [57]

Long Sutton, Spalding, Lincolnshire, PE12 9LE
(½ mile (¾ km) off the A17 in Long Sutton)
Tel: 0406 363833
Proprietors: Peter and Julie Worth

Open: Every day from Easter till the end of October from 10.00 to 6.00

Admission Fees: £2.30 adults, £1.20 children under 16 years, £2.00 OAPs.
Party rates for groups of not less than 12 can be had on application

Additional Costs: None

Catering: There is a tea room seating 150, which serves homemade food
including salads and ploughman's lunches

Facilities for Children: There is an adventure playground, and a pets corner

Facilities for the Disabled: Full facilities are present

Restrictions: Dogs are restricted to the 5-acre (2-ha) car park

This is not simply a butterfly house; there are all sorts of things to see
and do. Certainly there is a butterfly house, said to be the largest in the
country. There are also a variety of creepy crawlies to see, such as
scorpions and spiders. The whole place covers 12 acres (5 ha) and last
year 150,000 visitors, 24,000 of them schoolchildren came to see the
collection. Apart from the invertebrates there are farm animals, outdoor
nature trails, conservation gardens, wildflower meadows including a
whole acre (½ ha) of Cowslips, and an attractive feature is a
conservation pond. Thirty-seven species of British and tropical
butterflies are bred here and there is a resident entomologist and a
schoolroom for educational visits. One can get an education pack and a
nature trail leaflet.

utterfly Park

Something for everyone, Whatever the weather.

Long Sutton, Lincolnshire

**Enjoy a visit to one of Britain's largest indoor tropical gardens.
Relax and observe hundreds of exotic butterflies amongst a wealth of tropical plants and foliage**

Insectarium: *Compelling exhibits such as Scorpions and Tarantulas.*

Farm Walk: *Visit the numerous farm animals and Pets Corner.*

Butterfly & Bee Gardens: *Designed to attract native species.*

Gift Shop: *An excellent range of gifts.*

Adventure Playground: *A mini assault course for the children.*

Wild Flower Meadows: *An abundance of British wild flowers.*

Tea Room: *Enjoy delicious home made refreshments.*

Disabled visitors welcome—good access to all facilities.

OPEN DAILY—March 21st-October 31st, 10 a.m.-5 p.m.

Admissions — Adults £2.30, OAPs £1.75, Children (under 16) £1.20

FOLLOW THE AA SIGNS OFF THE A17 IN LONG SUTTON

Special Party Rates available from: Butterfly Park, Long Sutton, Lincolnshire PE12 9LE. Telephone (0406) 363833

Skegness Natureland, Marine Zoo and Seal Sanctuary [58]

North Parade, Skegness, Lincolnshire
(At the north end of the sea front in Skegness)
Tel: 0754 4345
Proprietor: J.K.B. Yeadon

Open: Every day except Christmas Day, Boxing Day and New Year's Day from 10.00. In winter the gates close at 5.00, in spring and autumn at 6.00, and in the summer at 8.00

Admission Fees: £1.80 adults, 90p children under 16 years, 80p OAPs. Party rates for groups of 20: £1.50 adults, 75p children

Additional Costs: None

Catering: There is a kiosk that sells drinks, sweets, crisps and ice cream

Facilities for Children: Pets corner

Facilities for the Disabled: All exhibits are accessible to wheelchairs except for one part of the reptile house

Restrictions: Dogs are not allowed in the Floral Palace, and elsewhere they must be kept on a lead. Only animals in the pets corner may be fed, and then only with food obtained from the gift shop. Children must be well supervised

Although this collection is very small in terms of the area that it covers, it is surprising what there is to see. There is a tropical house containing crocodiles, snakes, tarantulas, scorpions and other reptiles and invertebrates. There is an aquarium full of fish, including local marine life forms. There is the Floral Palace, over 170 feet (52 m) long which houses tropical butterflies and birds in a beautiful miniature jungle, and outside there is a collection of seals and penguins. Finally, there is a Rainbow Trout exhibit. Much work has been done here with seals, and long before they started dying in large numbers on the east coast, Skegness was rescuing injured and baby seals, caring for them, and where possible, returning them to the wild. I forgot to say that there is also a small island housing chipmunks, while in the water surrounding it are a number of fish. Teachers interested in doing projects here may make a free visit prior to taking children in order to prepare worksheets.

Kentish Town City Farm [59]

1 Cressfield Close, Grafton Road, London, NW5 4BN
Tel: 01 482 2861
Proprietor: Kentish Town City Farm Ltd

Open: Every day from 10.00 to 5.00

Admission Fees: None

Additional Costs: None

Catering: There is a cafe

Facilities for Children: There is a room for parties of children

Facilities for the Disabled: The site is accessible by wheelchairs

Restrictions: No dogs are allowed

This is a working farm, one of many around Britain, which ought to be visited by everyone who lives in towns. There are a number of farm animals to be seen.

The London Butterfly House [60]

Syon Park, Brentford, Middlesex, TW8 8JN
(from Junction 1 of the M3 join A316 or from the M4 join A315 and
follow the signs to Syon Park)
Tel: 01 560 7272
Proprietors: Dick Burgess and Clive Farrell

Open: While the clocks are on British Summer Time the Butterfly House is
open every day between 10.00 and 5.00. For the rest of the year it opens
between 10.00 and 3.30

Admission Fees: £1.90 adults, £1.10 children, £1.20 OAPs. A family ticket
for two adults and up to five children is £5.50. Disabled visitors in a
wheelchair pay the full rate, but the person pushing the chair is admitted free.
Party rate for a minimum of 20 is 95p

Additional Costs: Other facilities in Syon Park have separate charges, and
for details of these you should phone 01 560 0881 or 01 560 0882, but these
have nothing to do with the Butterfly House. Parking is free along the
entrance road

Catering: There are no facilities within the butterfly complex, but food may
be obtained elsewhere in Syon Park

Facilities for Children: None

Facilities for the Disabled: Special ramps and doors for wheelchairs

Restrictions: No dogs are allowed. They must be tied up outside, not carried,
due to the heat in the Butterfly House. Children under 12 must be
accompanied by an adult, and butterflies must not be handled

There are no toilets, picnic areas or food outlets within the butterfly
complex, but all these and much more are available in Syon Park itself,
which is full of a host of other attractions including an aquarium, rose
gardens, a motor museum, and the house and gardens themselves.
Syon Park Butterfly House is probably the best known of all. It has a
comprehensive collection of insects and other invertebrates, and a full-
time education officer. There is an education pack for teachers. Some
butterflies are bred here for use in genetic and evolution studies, and
the spectacular *Morpho* butterflies breed here regularly.

Edinburgh Butterfly Farm

Melville Nurseries, Lasswade, Nr Edinburgh, Midlothian. ☎ 031 663 4932

s lavish new butterfly farm was opened in April 1985 and he only one in Scotland. It was immediately popular with Scots who came in record numbers. The farm is set in the unds of Dobbies Garden Centre at Lasswade, near Dalkeith, ten minutes drive from the city centre. The Centre has its coach and car park with many other interesting displays the whole family.

ening Hours: April until October 31st only. 10 am - 6 pm nday to Friday: 10 am - 5.30 pm Saturday and Sunday.

Weymouth Butterfly Farm

Lodmoor Country Park, Greenhill, Weymouth, Dorset DTX 7SX. ☎ (0305) 783311

The Weymouth Butterfly Farm is the newest attraction to come to the ever expanding Lodmoor Country Park on the outskirts of town but within yards of the beach. The deep tropical jungle is set right next to the main Weymouth Car and Coach Park, other attractions such as a bird sanctuary and Sealife Centre are adjacent to the Farm.

Opening Hours: April until October 31st only. 10 am - 5 pm 7 days a week.

Welcome to the Wonderful World of Butterflies

Whatever the weather, wander in a tropical jungle paradise of exotic plants, trees and flowers, enjoy watching hundreds of delicate, richly coloured free flying butterflies from all over the world. Observe and study the strange and weird life of unusual insects, photograph in safety dangerous scorpions, tarantulas and other rarely viewed inhabitants of this fascinating habitat. Listen to splashing falls, see glistening tropical pools filled with giant waterlillies and a wonderful variety of colourful fish all surrounded by lush jungle vegetation. A visit not to be missed, all viewed in one huge ingeniously constructed indoor paradise, the largest in Britain. Superb educational facilities always available.

London Butterfly House

Syon Park, Brentford, Middlesex.
☎ 01 560 7272

et in its own medieval meadow in the middle of Syon Park. he of London's most popular parks and stately homes. The utterfly House was the first to be opened, and sitting as it is n the banks of the River Thames, has always been popular for ay trips. Also within the park is a Motor Museum. Garden entre and large picnic areas.

pening Hours: Open all year except Christmas period. British ummer Time 10 am - 5 pm: Winter Time 10 am - 3.30 pm.

Stratford-upon-Avon Butterfly Farm

Tramway Walk, Stratford-upon-Avon, Warwickshire. ☎ (0789) 299288

The newest and largest butterfly farm in the world sits splendidly within a few hundred yards of both coach station and theatre and also boasts of "Insect City", one of the most comprehensive insect displays in the UK. featuring the World's Biggest Spider.

Opening Hours: Open all year except Christmas period. British Summer Time 10 am - 5 pm: Winter Time 10 am - 3.30 pm.

"BRINGING BUTTERFLIES BACK TO BRITAIN..."

Guisborough Grange Wildlife Park [61]

Guisborough, Northampton
(The park is ¼ mile (400 m) from the village)
Tel: 0604 740278
Proprietors: Mr and Mrs Vince

Open: Every day except Christmas Day from 10.00 to 6.00, or dusk in winter

Admission Fees: £2.00 adults, £1.00 children under 16 years, 75p OAPs. Party rate for groups of 20 is a flat £1.50

Additional Costs: None. Car parking is free

Catering: There is a cafeteria and an ice cream stall

Facilities for Children: None

Facilities for the Disabled: There is a toilet for the disabled

Restrictions: Dogs are allowed if they are kept on leads, but feeding the animals is forbidden

In 30 acres (12 ha) of parkland surrounded by superb panoramic views, you can meet at close quarters many species of big cats, owls, deer, waterfowl, monkeys, bats and lots of other exotic birds and mammals. There is a daily falconry display, and lessons are held in falconry and the management of birds of prey. Some of the animals in this collection are used in film and television work.

BANHAM ZOO

Over 20 acres of wildlife —

Spend an exciting day amongst —
Snow Leopards, Zebras, Maned Wolves, Flamingoes, Llamas, Sealions, Otters, Owls, Chimpanzees and monkeys galore!

Licenced Cafeteria, Picnic areas, childrens play areas, ample free parking and Farm shop, Garden Centre, Putting Green all adjoin the zoo, plus Car Boot Sale every Sunday

Open Daily 10am - 6.30pm (or dusk if earlier)

Twixt Attleborough & Diss, between Norwich & Bury St. Edmunds on the B1113

The Grove, Banham, Norfolk, NR16 2HB *Tel:* **Quidenham (095 387) 476**

Banham Zoo and Monkey Sanctuary [62]

The Grove, Banham, Norfolk, NR16 2HE
(Between Norwich and Bury St Edmunds on the B1113)
Tel: 0953 87476
Proprietor: Banham Zoo Ltd

Open: Every day except Christmas Day and Boxing Day from 10.00 to 6.30, or dusk in winter

Admission Fees: £3.00 adults, £1.50 children between 3 and 16 years, £2.00 OAPs. Party rates: £2.00 adults, £1 children, £1.50 OAPs. These are the rates for 1989

Additional Costs: None

Catering: There is a cafeteria and a tea room

Facilities for Children: There are children's play areas including a Tots and Toddlers area for under 7s, and a Tarzan Trail. Children's meals can be obtained, and there is a pets corner

Facilities for the Disabled: Access to most exhibits is possible by wheelchair, which can be borrowed. Suitable toilets are provided

Restrictions: No dogs are allowed nor unaccompanied children, and the feeding of animals is forbidden

Though Banham Zoo has been in existence for only about twenty years, it has won for itself quite a reputation in that time, especially for its primate breeding programme. Ninety per cent of the animals in the collection are captive bred. It is a real pleasure to see a collection that does not bother with lions and tigers but concentrates instead on other, often less well-known species. The monkey island is particularly attractive. Just outside the zoo itself are various other attractions such as a putting green, a garden centre, a tropical fish dealer and, of all things, regular car-boot sales at weekends.

Kilverstone Wildlife Park and Miniature Horse Stud [63]

Thetford, Norfolk
(1 mile (1½ km) east of Thetford, just off the A11)
Tel: 0842 5369
Proprietors: Lord and Lady Fisher

Open: Every day including Christmas Day from 10.00 to 6.30, or dusk in winter

Admission Fees: (1988) £2.50 adults, £1.90 OAPs, £1.50 children. Enquire about party discounts

Additional Costs: Train rides around part of the grounds. Children's amusements. Ample, free car parking within the grounds. Tokens from the kiosk in the adventure playground needed for rides

Catering: There is a cafeteria, and in the summer this is augmented by ice cream stalls, a barbecue and fast-food outlets

Facilities for Children: Children's meals are available in the cafeteria where high chairs may be borrowed. There is an adventure playground with all the usual features together with a super fort and bridge to play on. There is a Patting Area and a room where mothers can change their babies' nappies

Facilities for the Disabled: Invalid chairs are available, and there are special toilets. Ramps lead to most parts of the zoo

Restrictions: No dogs are allowed in the zoo though they may be exercised in the car park. Only food bought from special dispensers may be given to the animals, and unaccompanied children are not admitted

Furthest from the entrance is the Falabella Miniature Horse Stud. During the afternoon there is a show jumping exhibition, and there are also miniature donkeys and cattle. The major part of the zoo's collection contains only animals from Central and South America. The collection consists almost entirely of mammals and birds. The primate collection is superb, many of the animals living on islands in a lake. A tremendous amount of breeding of common and endangered species is a feature of Kilverstone. There is a small walk-through jungle containing South American birds. The Education Centre is excelllent.

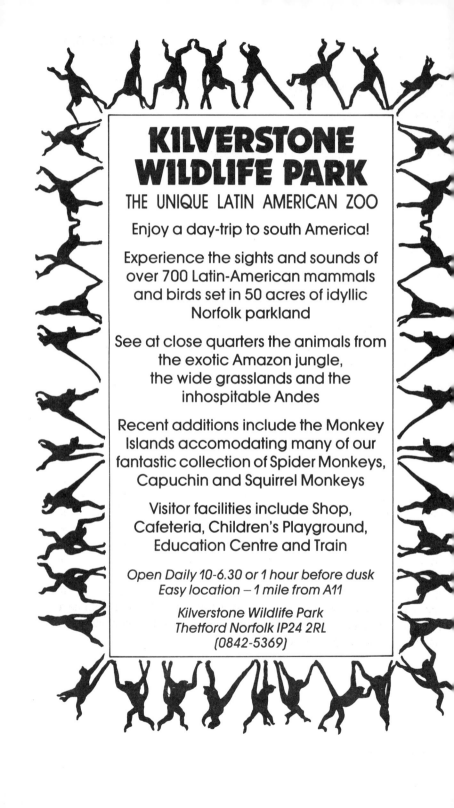

Thrigby Hall Wildlife Gardens [64]

Filby, Great Yarmouth, Norfolk, NR29 3DR
(1 mile (1½ km) south of Filby on the A1064 Acle to Caister road)
Tel: 0493 77477
Proprietor: Thrigby Hall Wildlife Gardens Ltd

Open: Every day from 10.00 to 5.00 or one hour before dusk

Admission Fees: £1.50 adults,£1.00 children (under 16 years). Party rates: £1.70 OAPs. Party rates: £1.80 adults, 90p children, £1.50 OAPs

Additional Costs: None

Catering: The cafeteria is open between Easter and October

Facilities for Children: There are play areas for children

Facilities for the Disabled: Wheelchairs can go everywhere, and one is available if required

Restrictions: No dogs are allowed, though they can be exercised in the car park in which case there is unlimited re-entry for dog owners. No feeding of the animals

The collection at Thrigby Hall specialises in animals from Asia, a region rich in interesting species such as the Binturong, the Snow Leopard and the Sumatran Tiger, all of which can be seen here. Other fascinating species on display are the Green Peafowl, which are far rarer in captivity than the common blue. The bird collection is a good one and so is the display of reptiles, and if you think muggers are close shaven and wear scruffy leather jackets, feast your eyes on Thrigby's Muggers, or Marsh Crocodiles as they are sometimes called. They are the only ones in Britain, as are the Hog Badgers. Thrigby Hall is interesting in itself, not least for its reputation for being haunted. Though the ghosts have not been seen for some time, curiously many outside doors and gates have been found open in the mornings!

Cotswold Wildlife Park [65]

Burford, Oxfordshire, OX8 4JW
(2 miles (3 km) south of Burford on the A361)
Tel: 099382 3006
Proprietor: Cotswold Wildlife Park Ltd

Open: Every day except Christmas Day from 10.00 to 6.00 or dusk in winter

Admission Fees: £2.70 adults, £1.60 children aged 4 to 16, £1.60 OAPs. Party rates for a minimum of 20 people are £2.20 adults, £1.25 children

Additional Costs: Train rides are 50p. Brass rubbings cost 60p and 30p. Car parking is free

Catering: There is a cafeteria/restaurant as well as ice cream and confectionery kiosks

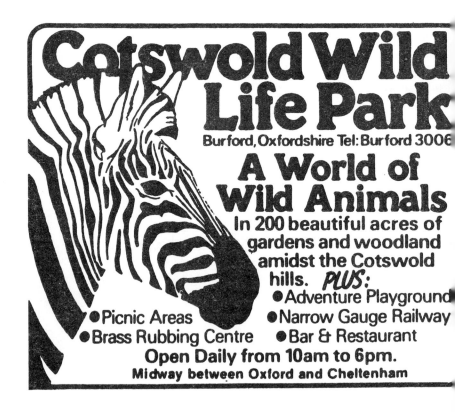

Facilities for Children: Children's meals are available. There are baby changing rooms and a limited number of pushchairs

Facilities for the Disabled: There are full facilities for the disabled, and some wheelchairs

Restrictions: Dogs are allowed only on leads. The feeding of animals is forbidden, and children must be accompanied by someone over the age of 16

Cotswold Wildlife Park has an interesting collection of animals from big cats to scorpions. It has received awards for breeding Black Storks, Meerkats, Humboldt Penguins, Lappet Faced Vultures and Great Indian Hornbills, and in addition they have had many other breeding successes. The animals are frequently in open enclosures, usually separated from the public by moats rather than unsightly fences. One can see here the only breeding pair of Black Storks in the country. Information packs are available for students, and there are three lecture rooms where the staff can talk to schools or other groups.

Shropshire Country World [66]

Yockleton, Shrewsbury, Shropshire, SY5 9PU
(On the B4386 west of Shrewsbury, 4 miles
(6½ km) from the Royal Shrewsbury Hospital)
Tel: 074384 217
Proprietors: Mr and Mrs Stephen Bromley

Open: Every day between Easter and the end of October between 10.00 and 6.00, or 5.00 in October

Admission Fees: (1988) £2.30 adults, £1.30 children between 4 and 16 years, £1.95 OAPs. Party rates for groups of over 15: £1.85. School parties and children's parties are £1.15 per head

Additional Costs: None

Catering: There is a cafe that sells homemade refreshments and ice cream

Facilities for Children: A high chair is available, and mother and baby facilities should be ready for the 1989 season

Facilities for the Disabled: There is good access to attractions including the farm ride, and a wheelchair is available if required. There is a toilet for the disabled

Restrictions: No dogs are allowed on the main site; there is an exercise area adjacent to the car park

This is a large farm and countryside collection which includes a farm animal centre. There is also a large tropical butterfly house. Conservation and landscaping projects are currently being undertaken with grant aid from the Countryside Commission. A school room is on the site, and teachers' information can be had on request. A guide is included with the price of entry, who links a school visit with the school's project. Tractor and trailer rides take visitors out into the rural parts of the farm. There is a traditional English meadow, a duck pond and a fish pool. Children can meet farm animals at the farm centre.

Cricket St Thomas Wildlife Park [67]

Estate Office, Cricket St Thomas, Chard, Somerset, TA20 4DD
(The entrance drive is on the A30, 3 miles (5 km) east of Chard and 5 miles (8 km) west of Crewkerne)
Tel: 046030 755
Proprietor: Cricket St Thomas Wildlife Park is owned by a partnership

Open: Every day from 10.00 to 6.00 in summer and 5.00, or dusk in winter

Admission Fees: £3.50 adults, £2.50 children between the ages of 3 and 14 years, £2.50 OAPs. Party rates for a minimum of 20: £3.00 adults, £2.00 children. Special rates for parties of disabled visitors are available on application. (These are 1988 prices)

Additional Costs: Train rides cost 50p each way

Catering: There is a licensed self-service restaurant and a tearoom. There are also kiosks selling confectionery and hot and cold drinks, and a food bar/barbecue at the heavy horse centre

Facilities for Children: Children's meals are available in the self-service restaurant, and there is a children's fort and an adventure trail in the woodland area at the heavy horse centre

Facilities for the Disabled: While some areas are a bit steep and not too suitable for wheelchairs, in most places there are ramps. Toilets for the disabled are available

Restrictions: Dogs should be kept on leads and are not allowed in the paddock areas, on the train, or in the restaurant or food shop, except for guide dogs. Children should preferably be accompanied by an adult, and animals are not to be fed by the public

Cricket St Thomas must surely be the wildlife park for everyone. There are animals of all sorts from elephants to Quetzals, which are almost as rare in captivity as they are in the wild. The collection is superb and the setting is idyllic. Many of the birds are free flying, there are plenty of ducks and geese. There are Koi Carp and vultures and snakes. Breeding successes include Jaguars, Black Lemurs and White Fronted

Lemurs, Scarlet Macaws, Cottontop Tamarins, Emperor Tamarins and Trumpeter Swans. There are five species of lemur in the park. When you want a break from zoology you can visit the heavy horse centre and children's farm with its picturesque Georgian cottage and farm buildings, horse-drawn agricultural implements and free-ranging fowl and ducks. The television series 'To The Manor Born' was filmed here and a booklet describing the filming is available from the souvenir shop. There is a garden and farm-produce shop where you can buy delicious homemade ice cream, and there is so much else to see and do that you do need over a day to appreciate the place. Educational leaflets are available for purchase by teachers.

Ferne Animal Sanctuary [68]

Chard, Somerset
(1 mile (1½ km) off the A30, 3 miles (5 km) from Chard)
Tel: 0460 65214
Proprietor: Ferne Animal Sanctuary Trust

Open: Wednesdays, Saturdays, Sundays and Bank Holidays from 1 April to 30 September, from 2.00 to 5.00

Admission Fees: None

Additional Costs: None

Catering: Soft drinks and light refreshments are available

Facilities for Children: None

Facilities for the Disabled: There are ramps and special parking arrangements

Restrictions: No dogs are allowed, and animals may not be fed

At the beginning of the Second World War, the Duke and Duchess of Hamilton and Brandon realised that many service personnel, perhaps leaving home for the first time, would not be able to find homes for their pets. An invitation was broadcast on the BBC to anyone in this position, suggesting that these animals might like to spend the war on the Duke's estate in Dorset. Thus started the Ferne Animal Sanctuary. Nowadays it exists to provide homes for all domestic animals needing sanctuary. The Trust also owns a small island in the Orkneys as a seal sanctuary. There are about 250 animals at Ferne, ranging from gerbils to horses. The Trust is keen on wild life and arboreal conservation, and tries to show young people that there is more pleasure to be had from caring for animals than from torturing them or kicking them out of their home. Though there are no admission fees, the Trust would not refuse a small donation from visitors.

The Tropical Bird Gardens [69]

Rode, Bath, Somerset, BA3 6QW
(Between Bath and Warminster, off the A36)
Tel: 0373 830326
Proprietor: Rode Zoological Gardens Ltd

Open: Every day except for Christmas Day from 10.30 to 7.00 in summer and sunset in winter. There are no admissions after 6.00 in summer

Admission Fees: (1988) £2.30 adults, £1.20 children under 14 years, £1.90 OAPs. Party rates for groups of 25 or over: £1.90 adults, 95p children, £1.85 OAPs

Additional Costs: Steam train rides: 60p adults, 50p children, 40p party rate

Catering: In the summer there is a licensed cafeteria, and in winter light refreshments may be obtained from the gift shop

Facilities for Children: There is a children's play area, and in summer a pets corner

Facilities for the Disabled: There are wheelchairs for hire, a toilet for the disabled, and ramps where appropriate

Restrictions: No dogs are admitted, and children under 14 must be accompanied by an adult

When I first kept birds many years ago, a book written by Donald Risdon, who founded this collection, was my bible, and it was the first bird garden I ever visited to see how it should be done. Since then it has grown and developed and now houses a wide variety of birds. It has been responsible for the breeding for the first time in Britain of Scarlet Ibis and Umbrella Cockatoo, while numbers of other birds breed regularly such as macaws, flamingoes, Black Footed Penguins, cranes and waterfowl. This is a colourful collection of birds in lovely, natural surroundings. There is an information centre, and spotter packs and junior quizzes are available as aids to education.

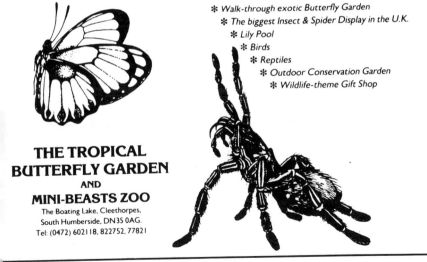

The Tropical Butterfly Gardens [70]

The Boating Lake, Cleethorpes, South Humberside, DN35 0AG
(On Cleethorpes sea front. Accessible from the A180, A46 and A16)
Tel: 0472 602118 or 0472 77821 or 0472 822752
Proprietor: Pro-Nature Ltd

Open: Every day except Christmas Day. April to October from 10.00 to 5.00, and from November to March from 10.00 to 3.30

Admission Fees: £1.40 adults, 80p for children under 3 years, £1.00 OAPs. School party rates (no minimum number) 75p. Family tickets for two adults and up to three children cost £3.75. Enquire about other party rates and evening openings

Additional Costs: None

Catering: Hungry Caterpillar snack bar

Facilities for Children: Accessible by pushchair and pram. Raised blocks in the educational display room for children to stand on so that they can actually see into the tanks of animals

Facilities for the Disabled: None specifically, but everywhere accessible by wheelchair

Restrictions: No dogs, and no smoking

The display is said to be the biggest and most varied in Britain. There is a large, walk-through jungle full of butterflies and moths, together with birds, tortoises and fish. Next to this is a room full of display tanks containing reptiles, amphibians and invertebrates. The Tropical Butterfly Gardens are very hot on conservation and education, and the parent company supplies entomological livestock to other butterfly gardens, zoos and collectors. There is a gift shop and an outdoor conservation garden, and the premises are adjacent to a Site of Special Scientific Interest, and a boating lake.

Heeley City Farm [71]

Richards Road, Heeley, Sheffield, S2 3DT
(1½ miles (2½ km) from the centre of Sheffield. Follow the A61 to
Chesterfield and turn left on to the B6347 at the Earl of Arundel
pub)
Tel: 0742 580482
Proprietor: Heeley City Farm Trust

Open: Every day of the year from 9.00 to 4.00

Admission Fees: None

Additional Costs: None

Catering: None available

Facilities for Children: Children are encouraged to meet small animals

Facilities for the Disabled: Wheelchair access to every part of the farm

Restrictions: None

I am all in favour of city farms as they present urban people with
opportunities that otherwise they would never have. Though I work in
London I live in the country, and it surprises me how Londoners go into
raptures over things I take for granted, like wild rabbits and trees in
autumn. If you have never been to a city farm, go and visit one; you will
enjoy it. They tend, by the nature of their work, to be scruffy places,
but they are really interesting. Heeley City Farm breeds various rare
breeds of pigs, sheep and cattle, and guided tours around the place can
be arranged. Where else could you meet two sheep called Maggie and
Vivian? There is also a Dexter cow named Louise and if you have never
met a Dexter, you have a treat in store as they are delightful animals.
There are also numbers of farmyard birds and perhaps less common are
the quail. There are also hives of bees. Numbers of otherwise
unemployed people work at the farm, and it holds adult education
classes in horse care, backyard farming and other similar topics.

There is a wildlife garden full of good things and a herb garden and
garden centre. Staff from the farm visit a number of places during the
year, from carnivals to junior schools to public libraries, in order to
publicise their work and for educational purposes.

Drayton Manor Park [72]

Tamworth, Staffordshire, B78 3TW
(On the A5/A4091)
Tel: 0827 287979
Proprietor: Drayton Manor Park Ltd

Open: Every day from Easter to October from 10.30 to 6.00, and from October to March from 11.00 to 4.00

Admission Fees: £1.50 adults, £1.00 children (under 16 years). Party rates: £1.00 adults, 60p children over 4 years, 40p children of 2 and 3 years, 60p OAPs. Enquire about day schools and ride payments

Additional Costs: £4.00 for a wristband for unlimited rides, or individual tickets for all rides. Car parking 30p

Catering: There is a fully licensed cafeteria, together with shops and kiosks

Facilities for Children: Children's facilities are available, but no pushchairs

Facilities for the Disabled: There are ramps, and toilets for the disabled, but no wheelchairs

Restrictions: No feeding of the animals

The zoo is only part of a Family Leisure Park, and admission to it is free after admission to the park has been paid, so there is plenty to do. The animal collection is not large, but is interesting. There is a new and enlarged reptile house, and new sealion and penguin pools, and there is a small working farm. Last year saw the opening of Natureland, a new activity, conservation and education display containing attractive and interesting nature trails. There are big cats and primates, and the reptiles collection is especially interesting, being one of the few in the country containing venomous animals.

Easton Farm Park [73]

**Easton, Wickham Market, Woodbridge, Suffolk,
IP13 0EQ**
(Turn off the A12 onto the B1116 to Framlingham and
follow the signs)
Tel: 0728 746475
Proprietor: Easton Farm Park is a private collection

Open: From Easter until the end of September between 10.30 and 6.00; the
last admission is at 4.30

Admission Fees: None

Catering: There is a tea room which serves light lunches and cream teas

Facilities for Children: There is a high chair in the tea room, there are baby
changing facilities, and there is a pets corner

Facilities for the Disabled: There are hard paths, wide doorways, a ramp to
the tea room, and toilets for the disabled

Restrictions: Dogs are only admitted on a lead

Easton Farm Park is part of a large working-farm complex. Here one
can see all sorts of traditional and modern farm animals. At the small
end there are pigs, goats, ponies, poultry, and ornamental peafowl and
pheasants. But to my mind it is the larger animals that are the more
interesting. The place started with the three animals that were always
known as the Suffolk Trinity, that is the Red Poll Cattle, the Suffolk
Sheep and the Suffolk Punch horses. These three traditionally provided
the nation's food from East Anglian farms. You can still see them here,
together with White Park Cattle, magnificent animals, little changed for
hundreds of years. If you thought that Victorian painters had a funny
idea about the proportions of cattle, have a look at these beasts, and
you will see why the artists painted them in that way. There are also
some English Longhorn Cattle, another of my favourite breeds. There
are other things of interest in this collection, such as traditional farm
machinery, but whatever else you do, don't miss the beautiful and
attractive Victorian dairy. You've never seen anything like it. It has
marble shelves, and a fountain to help keep the butter cool, and is just
what a dairy should be like and rarely is. It is easy to think that all the
animals are simply here to be stroked, but this is a working farm, and if

you are still one of the ever diminishing number of carnivores in this country and you still eat turkey at Christmas, you can order a fresh one from here and pick it up during Christmas week. It will taste infinitely better than one from a supermarket that has been killed, processed and frozen in a matter of a couple of hours, rather than being hung as a turkey should be, for a few days after it has been killed.

Norton Tropical Bird Gardens [74]

Norton, Bury St Edmunds, Suffolk IP31 3LE
(On the A1088 off the A45, 8 miles (13 km) east of Bury St Edmunds)
Tel: 0359 30957
Proprietors: Mr and Mrs D.W.G. Frost

Open: Every day from 11.00 to 6.00, or dusk in winter

Admission Fees: (1988) £2.00 adults, 75p children between 5 and 16 years, £1.50 OAPs. Party rates for 20 or more when pre-booked: £1.50 adults, 50p children, £1.20 OAPs

Additional Costs: None

Catering: There is a tearoom serving light refreshments, ice cream and other food

Facilities for Children: None

Facilities for the Disabled: None as such, but help is available for lifting wheelchairs up the very few steps

Restrictions: No dogs are allowed, nor unaccompanied children

Although this is a small collection of birds from various parts of the world, there are still over a hundred species to be seen, from the ubiquitous parrots to cranes, flamingoes, owls, pheasants and waterfowl together with many small species, some in walk-through aviaries. The bird keeper can buy stock here as well, together with cages, feeders, drinkers, books and other accessories. The gardens are colourful, especially in the spring and the autumn.

The Otter Trust [75]

Earsham, Bungay, Suffolk, NR35 2AF
(1 mile (1½ km) west of Bungay, just off the A143)
Tel: 0986 3470
Proprietor: The Otter Trust

Open: Every day from 1 April to 31 October from 10.30 to 6.00

Admission Fees: £2.50 adults, £1.00 children under 16 years, £1.75 OAPs, and there is no discount for parties

Additional Costs: None

Catering: There is a tearoom

Facilities for Children: None, apart from a playground

Facilities for the Disabled: There are suitable toilets

Restrictions: No dogs are allowed nor unaccompanied children, and feeding of the animals is forbidden

This is a highly specialised place, and as such, very interesting. If you want to see lots of animals of a number of species you are in danger of being very bored here; however, if you love otters, as most people in the country apparently do, then this is the place to visit. Otters in Britain have become very scarce indeed and the Otter Trust is doing something about it. These delightful animals are being bred here in order that they can be re-introduced to the wild, and considerable success is being achieved in this area. It is the only place in the country where European Otters are breeding. The enclosures are large and natural, and there is a nature trail. If otters are to succeed, education is essential, consequently there is an education officer and a lecture room together with information on the subject.

Tropical Butterflies (Barrow) [76]

Barrow, Bury St Edmunds, Suffolk, IP29 5BG
(1 mile (1½ km) south of the A45 between Newmarket and Bury
St Edmunds)
Tel: 0284 810859
Proprietor: Tropical Butterflies (Barrow) Ltd

Open: Every day from Easter to the end of October from 10.00 to 5.00

Admission Fees: £2.30 adults, £1.50 children between the ages of 5 and 15 years, £2.00 OAPs. Enquire about party rates for groups of 15 and over

Additional Costs: Steam train rides

Catering: There is a cafeteria

Facilities for Children: None

Facilities for the Disabled: The site is fully accessible to wheelchairs

Restrictions: No dogs are admitted

Walk-through butterfly jungles are hot and humid and full of good things to see. At Barrow there are plenty of free-flying exotic butterflies together with a few birds and reptiles. There is also a display of spiders and other invertebrates, as well as a demonstration beehive, safely behind glass, where one can watch the complex and fascinating life of these incredible little insects. Don't just glance at them as you walk past; stop and watch for a while and you will discover that the bees are not just rushing about aimlessly as you first thought. Guided tours for educational visits can be arranged.

Birdworld [77]

Holt Pound, Farnham, Surrey GU10 4LD
(3 miles (5 km) south of Farnham on the A325)
Tel: 0420 22140
Proprietors: The Harvey Family

Open: Every day except Christmas Day from 9.30 to 6.00, or dusk in winter

Admission Fees: £1.90 adults, £1.10 children between 3 and 15 years, £1.65 OAPs. Party rates for 20 people or over are a flat £1.35. These are the prices for 1988

Additional Costs: Safari ride 40p

Catering: There is a cafeteria, an ice cream parlour and a safari shop

Facilities for Children: Babies' room

Facilities for the Disabled: There are ramps and wide paths for wheelchairs, which are available, and toilets for the disabled

Restrictions: No pets are allowed

This collection of birds contains everything from Ostriches to hummingbirds, taking in along the way, pelicans, tragopans, touracos and tanagers. It really is worth a visit if you are at all birdy, and when you really cannot look at another feather, next door to Birdworld is Underwater World which holds a most interesting collection of freshwater and marine fish. There is also The Owl's Nest, a natural history bookshop, and surrounding Birdworld is the Alice Holt Forest, 2000 acres (810 ha) of it interspersed with tracks. It is rich in wildlife and there is an information centre. Education facilities at Birdworld include information sheets. There have been many breeding successes including Casqued Hornbills and Kookaburras.

Busbridge Lakes Ornamental Waterfowl [78]

Busbridge Lakes, Hambledon Road, Godalming, Surrey, GU8 4AY

(1½ miles (2½ km) from Godalming on the Hambledon road)

Tel: 04868 21955

Proprietor: Mrs F.C. Douetil

Open: From 11.00 to 5.30 on the following dates: Good Friday, 24 March, then every day until 2 April, 30 April, 1 May, 28 May, 29 May, 20 August then every day till 28 August. Parties may visit any day by prior arrangement

Admission Fees: £2.00 adults, £1.20 children between 5 and 14 years, £1.20 OAPs

Additional Costs: None

Catering: Light refreshments are available at weekends and on Bank Holidays only

Facilities for Children: None

Facilities for the Disabled: None

Restrictions: No dogs are allowed

Busbridge Lakes is a Surrey beauty spot listed as a Heritage Garden, especially mentioned for its follies, grottoes and caves. The major part of the 40-acre (16-ha) park is enclosed, allowing visitors to walk among the ornamental waterfowl, peafowl and pheasants, which are shown to advantage with three lakes and old specimen trees forming a background. There is also a flock of Jacob's Four Horned Sheep. The site is rich in native wildlife. The collection claims no conservation achievements, and there are no educational facilities.

Chessington World of Adventures [79]

Leatherhead Road, Chessington, Surrey, KT9 2NE
(2 miles (3 km) from Junction 9 of the M25 or A3)
Tel: 03727 27227
Proprietor: The Pearson Group

Open: Every day except Christmas Day, 10.00 to 6.00 in summer, but closing at 4.00 between November and March

Admission Fees: £6.25 adults, £5.25 children under 15 years. Party rates (minimum 15) £5.25 adults, £4.25 children and OAPs. Enquire about special school rates

Additional Costs: None

Catering: There is a restaurant and a variety of refreshment outlets available throughout the park

Facilities for Children: Children's meals are available in the restaurant. There is a mother and baby room, and children's rides and animals are to be found in the Children's Zoo

Facilities for the Disabled: Disabled facilities are available including access to rides. Toilets for the disabled

Restrictions: No dogs. No feeding of animals

Some years ago Chessington Zoo was a clapped out, decidedly seedy collection of animals together with a few equally tatty entertainment features. If that is how you remember it, go again, and be surprised. Chessington is no longer just a zoo. If the whole family is not absorbed by animals they can enjoy themselves in Calamity Canyon, or The Mystic East, or any one of the many other fascinating parts of the park. One admission ticket covers all, which is why the prices are higher than for most zoos. That does not mean that the zoo is any the less worthwhile. It has bred Ocelots, Andean Condors, De Brazza Monkeys and others. You can see Barbary Apes, for which Gibraltar is famous, and which are not apes at all. The zoo boasts the second best gorilla enclosure in the country, and those for the gibbons, the lions and the tigers are particularly roomy. The guide book is especially informative and well laid out, which is quite a feat when those of most zoos are glossy and spectacular.

Deen City Farm [80]

1 Batsworth Road, Mitcham, Surrey
(Between Colliers Wood and Mitcham cricket green)
Tel: 01 648 1461
Proprietor: Deen City Farm is run as a registered charity

Open: Every day except Mondays, unless they are Bank Holidays

Admission Fees: None, but there is a box for donations at the gate

Additional Costs: None

Catering: There is a cafe and a farm shop

Facilities for Children: Children's meals are available, and pushchairs, and children's toilets

Facilities for the Disabled: There is a toilet for the disabled, and riding for the disabled facilities

Restrictions: No dogs are allowed, and neither are unaccompanied children under the age of 7

This is a working city farm which keeps rare breeds of farm animals. There is an education officer and a class room, and one can obtain worksheets, and watch demonstrations.

Underwater World [81]

Holt Pound, Farnham, Surrey, GU10 4LD
(3 miles (5 km) south of Farnham on the A325)
Tel: 0420 22668
Proprietors: The Harvey Family

Open: Every day except Christmas Day from 9.30 to 5.30 in summer and till 4.30 in winter

Admission Fees: 60p adults, 35p children between 3 and 15 years, 45p for groups of 20 or more

Additional Costs: None

Catering: None

Facilities for Children: None

Facilities for the Disabled: There are ramps where necessary, and wide paths

Restrictions: No dogs are allowed, nor unaccompanied children

Sine the aquarium was built in 1977 many advances have been made in the keeping of tropical fish. Devices such as bio-water towers, protein skimmers and ultra violet sterilisers produce a very clear and extremely healthy environment, making for a better display, and healthier fish and plants. Don't rush past what might appear to be empty tanks, for whereas many of the inhabitants are brightly coloured, many more are superbly disguised and need searching for. Visitors can see here the only breeding group of Philippine Ground Sharks in the country. When you have finished with the fish there is Birdworld next door, a natural history bookshop, and 2000 acres (810 ha) of the Alice Holt Forest in which you can walk and see all sorts of wild animals and plants.

Gatwick Zoo and Gatwick Butterfly and Tropical Gardens [82]

Charlwood, Surrey, RH6 0EG
(3 miles (5 km) west of Gatwick airport. Follow
the signs to Charlwood and then the zoo)
Tel: 0293 862312
Proprietors: T.E. and H.S. Thorpe

Open: Every day from Easter to the end of October from 10.30 to 6.00

Admission Fees: (1988) A combined ticket to the zoo, the aviaries, and the butterfly and tropical gardens costs £3.00 adults, £1.50 children from 3 to 14 years, £2.25 OAPs

Additional Costs: None stated

Catering: There is a cafeteria, and ice creams are available

Facilities for Children: Children's meals may be obtained and there is a pets corner and a playground

Facilities for the Disabled: There are no steps so everywhere is accessible, and toilets for the disabled are there for use

Restrictions: No dogs, no unaccompanied children and no feeding of animals except with prepared food sold at the zoo

This is a small, private collection packed with all sorts of good things. There are no large mammals such as elephants, rhinos or big cats, but there is a splendid collection of birds and many small mammals. The zoo has bred a number of species of parrots, otters, monkeys, and others including those delightful little characters, Meerkats. It is the only zoo to have bred the endangered Military Macaw. The enclosures are very spacious and the monkeys are attractively displayed on an island. Children in parties receive a discount of 10 per cent, and their teacher gets in free. There is a schools pack for those that want it, free entry to their schools competition, and free talks in the education building.

The Wildfowl Trust [83]

Arundel Castle Park, Mill Road, Arundel, Sussex, BN18 9PB
(From the main entrance of Arundel Castle travel along Mill Road,
and the reserve is opposite the lake in the Castle Park, less than 1
mile (1½ km) from the town centre)
Tel: 0903 883355
Proprietor: The Wildfowl Trust

Open: Every day except Christmas Day, between 9.30 and 5.30, or until 4.00
in winter

Admission Fees: (1988) £2.20 adults, £1.10 children between 4 and 16
years, £1.40 OAPs. Party rates for groups of 20 or more: £1.80. Enquire
about special rates for school parties

Additional Costs: None

Catering: There is a licensed restaurant

Facilities for Children: Children can feed the birds. There are checklists and
illustrated signs, and level paths make the pushing of prams easy

Facilities for the Disabled: Free wheelchairs are available. There is easy
access to hides, and talks and tactile exhibitions can be arranged

Restrictions: No dogs are allowed in the reserve

Arundel Castle and the wooded hillsides of Offham Hanger form the
magnificent backdrop to this, the Wildfowl Trust's newest reserve. Its
55 acres (22 ha) contain about 1200 wildfowl, with Swan Lake at the
centre. Observation hides overlook ponds, reed beds and wader
scrapes. Depending on the season you may see Water Rail, Teal, snipe,
Greenshank, Redshank and Green Sandpiper. There is an education
wing to the spacious reception building, with a cinema cum lecture
room, together with an exhibition area and a large viewing gallery.

The Wildfowl Trust [84]

Washington Waterfowl Park, District 15, Washington, Tyne and Wear, NE38 8LB
(650 yards (600 m) from Barmston village)
Tel: 091 416 5454
Proprietor: The Wildfowl Trust

Open: Every day except Christmas Eve and Christmas Day, from 9.30 to 5.00 in summer, and one hour before dusk in winter

Admission Fees: (1988) £2.00 adults, 90p children between 4 and 16 years, £1.30 OAPs. Party rates for groups of 20 or more: £1.50. Enquire about rates for schools groups

Additional Costs: None

Catering: There is a tea room

Facilities for Children: There is a special play area, and checklists of the birds to be seen, and children may feed the birds

Facilities for the Disabled: There are free wheelchairs, suitable toilet facilities, specially modified observation hides, a Braille map, talks, and tactile exhibits

Restrictions: No dogs are allowed

Here on the delightfully landscaped hillside sloping down to the River Wear, conditions are ideal for both birds and visitors. In the woods there are feeding stations and in the wild areas comfortable hides enable you to watch the 1200 water birds from some 110 species, from all over the world. There is also a flock of Chilean Flamingoes, all named after characters from Catherine Cookson novels. Talks and films can be provided by arrangement, and worksheets are available for educational visits.

Birmingham Nature Centre
[85]

Pershore Road, Edgbaston, Birmingham, B5 7RL
(The centre is near the BBC Pebble Mill Studios)
Tel: 021 472 7775
Proprietor: City of Birmingham/Museums and Art Gallery

Open: Every day from March to October between 10.00 and 5.00

Admission Fees: None

Additional Costs: None

Catering: There is a cafeteria

Facilities for Children: All areas are accessible to pushchairs

Facilities for the Disabled: All areas are accessible to wheelchairs. There is a toilet for the disabled

Restrictions: No dogs are allowed, nor bicycles. Ball games are forbidden and visitors must not feed the animals

This is an absorbing, small collection of animals, plants and habitats such as are to be found in Britain or northwest Europe. One can see limestone grassland, marshland and woodland biotopes. Barn Owls have been bred here and released into the wild. There is a teacher on the site with a classroom for educational visits, and museum displays augment and develop biological themes.

Stratford Upon Avon Butterfly Farm and Jungle Safari [86]

The Tramway, Swans Nest Lane, Stratford Upon Avon, Warwickshire, CV37 7LS
(Next to the River Avon across the footbridge in the centre of Stratford. The Tramway is situated off the A34)
Tel: 0789 299288
Proprietor: The Stratford Upon Avon Butterfly Farm Ltd

Open: Every day except Christmas Eve and Christmas Day, from 10.00 till 6.00 in summer, and till dusk in winter. Last admissions during the summer are at 5.30

Admission Fees: £1.95 adults, £1.50 children and OAPs, £5.50 for a family ticket for two adults and up to two children. A further four children can be admitted using this ticket for a further 50p per child. Party rates: £1.70 adults, £1.30 children and OAPs; 50p children under 5 years; 70p nursery children (under 5 years) and accompanying adults; £1.30 school groups of older children and their teachers

Additional Costs: None

Catering: None, but available nearby

Facilities for Children: All displays are accessible by pushchair

Facilities for the Disabled: All displays are accessible by wheelchair

Restrictions: No dogs are allowed, and no unaccompanied children under 10 years

Stratford Upon Avon Butterfly Farm was opened by David Bellamy in 1985. It incorporates a magnificent water garden complete with a spring and a waterfall, and a most distinctive water lily pool. The visitor can wander in a tropical jungle amongst several hundred butterflies from all over the world. In addition there are birds, lizards, tree frogs and fish all living together. There is also a room full of other invertebrates such as spiders and stick insects. Finally, the visitor can explore the possibility of developing his or her own butterfly garden after visiting the British and European butterfly area.

Twycross Zoo [87]

Atherstone, Warwickshire, CV9 3PX
(On the A444, Burton to Nuneaton road, which is
directly off the M42)
Tel: 0827 880250
Proprietor: East Midlands Zoological Society

Open: Every day except Christmas Day from 10.00 to 6.00 in summer and
4.00 in winter

Admission Fees: £2.60 adults, £1.30 for children of 3 years and over, £2.00
OAPs. Party rates: (when there is a minimum of 25) £2.00 adults, £1.00
children (though they are charged only 50p if they are under 3 years)

Additional Costs: Parking is 30p, admission to the reptile house costs 10p,
and the summer attractions are all 30p

Catering: There are self-service cafeterias and a licensed bar open during the summer, but in the winter there is only a tea bar

Facilities for Children: Children's meals are available, and a high chair. There is an adventure playground

Facilities for the Disabled: The flat gravel paths make for easy walking and most of the animal houses have sloping entrances so access is no problem. There are suitable toilets for the physically handicapped

Restrictions: No dogs are allowed, children must be accompanied by an adult at all times, and feeding the animals is not permitted

Although Twycross is best known for its collection of primates, which ranges from gorillas to tiny South American prosimians, there is much else to see. There are elephants and giraffes, sealions and birds, and a small but most interesting reptile house. The zoo is small, which means that one is not likely to become worn out with walking, and most of the exhibits have indoor viewing areas for visitors. During the summer there are all sorts of special attractions such as Chimps' picnics, Donkey rides, elephants' bath time and so on. There is a good education department which can provide a number of different talks, specially geared to different groups of visitors, and teachers may obtain a whole range of information packs and so on, which cost from a few pence each to over £2. Teaching sessions are also charged for.

The Lions of Longleat Safari Park [88]

Warminster, Wiltshire, BA12 7NJ
(On the A362, halfway between Warminster and Frome)
Tel: 09853 328
Proprietor: Lions of Longleat Ltd

Open: Every day from March to the end of October between 10.00 and 5.30

Admission Fees: £3.80 adults, £2.50 children under 15 years, £3.00 OAPs. Enquire about party rates

Additional Costs: There are various additional charges for other attractions at Longleat

Catering: There are two restaurants and a pub, together with various kiosks

Facilities for Children: Specifically, none, but the park is suitable for all ages

Facilities for the Disabled: Toilet facilities are available for the disabled

Restrictions: No dogs are allowed within the Safari Park, but free kennels are available to leave them in

If you have never been to a safari park, you should realise that it is not just about lions. There are all sorts of large mammals to see. Most of them have to be viewed from a closed car as you drive round the grounds, but some can be seen on foot and others from a water safari boat. There is also a pets corner and a reptile house, and in the garden centre, a butterfly display. One can watch a parrot show, and by the time you read this, the new exhibit featuring the only white tiger in Britain should be open. For those members of the family who are not interested in animals, there is Longleat House itself together with its gardens, amusement arcades, a Doctor Who exhibition and much else.

All the species of animal in the Safari Park breed there with the exception of two, and specimens are sent to other collections from time to time. Lions do so well that it has been calculated that there are now more lions in Britain than in Africa, though not all are at Longleat!

The Domestic Fowl Trust [89]

**Honeybourne Pastures, Honeybourne, Evesham,
Worcestershire, WR11 5QJ**
(In the centre of Honeybourne village)
Tel: 0386 833038
Proprietors: M. and V. Roberts

Open: Every day except Friday from 10.30 to 5.00

Admission Fees: £1.50 adults, 75p children under 16 years

Additional Costs: None

Catering: There is a tearoom

Facilities for Children: There is a high chair available in the tearoom. There is an adventure playground and a children's farm

Facilities for the Disabled: Ramps make access easy for wheelchairs

Restrictions: Dogs are allowed only if kept on a lead

Visitors can walk round 10 acres (4 ha) of small paddocks and ponds containing some 130 breeds of domestic ducks, geese, turkeys, fowl and quail. If you always thought that such birds were boring, you really should visit the Domestic Fowl Trust, for they are all fascinating and beautiful animals. And if you decide to take up the keeping of these birds, you can even buy them and the necessary equipment from here. There is a conservation centre, and educational leaflets may be obtained by teachers. All the birds are properly labelled, and a slide and tape set is available. This collection is well worth a visit. After all one can see lions and tigers all over the place, but these breeds are part of our disappearing heritage, and must be maintained, not just for aesthetic or historical reasons, but as a gene bank as well.

West Midland Safari and Leisure Park [90]

Spring Grove, Bewdley, Worcestershire, DY12 1LF
(On the main A456 between Kidderminster and Bewdley)
Tel: 0299 402114 or 0299 402631
Proprietor: West Midland Safari and Leisure Park Ltd

Open: Every day from April to the end of October between 10.00 and 5.00

Admission Fees: (1988) £6.00 adults, £5.00 children from 4 to 16 years, £5.00 OAPs. Party rates for groups of 20 or over: £4.00 adults, £3.50 children, £3.00 OAPs

Additional Costs: None. The entrance fee covers all rides, shows etc.

Catering: There are a burger bar, a farmhouse kitchen, and kiosks selling hot potatoes, chips, ice cream, candy floss and tea and coffee. There is also a licensed bar

Facilities for Children: Children's meals are available

Facilities for the Disabled: There are toilets for the disabled, and wheelchairs can get everywhere

Restrictions: No dogs are allowed in the animal reserve. Kennels are provided for this part of the drive. Anywhere else dogs may be taken on a lead

One can find many large mammals here, most of them roaming freely. Those that might decide to eat visitors are in enclosures. Many species have been bred here such as Giraffes, Lions, Tigers, zebra, deer, wolves, wallabies, Emus, Rhesus Monkeys and Llamas. There are also White Rhinos, majestic Ankole Cattle, Père David's Deer and elephants. There is a reptile house, performing sealions and a pets corner. On top of that there are train rides, big dippers, swing boats and heaps of similar amusements, set in a separate part of the grounds. There is an education centre where teachers' can find guide books, project books and teachers packs. As with other safari parks, one drives around the grounds in a vehicle.

Guernsey Zoo [91]

La Villiaze, St Andrews, Guernsey, Channel Islands
(Near the airport)
Tel: 0481 39176
Proprietor: The Zoological Trust of Guernsey

Open: Every day from 10.00 to 6.00 in summer, though the last admission is at 5.00, and until 4.00 in winter

Admission Fees: No figures given

Additional Costs: None

Catering: There is a cafeteria

Facilities for Children: None

Facilities for the Disabled: Full facilities are available, together with wheelchairs which may be borrowed

Restrictions: No dogs are allowed, and no feeding of the animals

This is a small, interesting collection which contains the only breeding group of Small Hairy Armadillo in the world. There are also Meerkats and gibbons, Squirrel Monkeys and Capuchin Monkeys as well as Two Toed Sloths, Servals, Coatis and others. There is an education officer and a classroom which can be used by school groups.

Jersey Wildlife Preservation Trust [92]

Les Augres Manor, Trinity, Jersey, Channel Islands
(3 miles (5 km) north of St Helier)
Tel: 0534 61949
Proprietor: Jersey Wildlife Preservation Trust

Open: Every day except Christmas Day from 10.00 to 6.00, or till dusk in winter

Admission Fees: (1988) £2.60 adults, £1.60 children under 14 years, £2.00 OAPs. Enquire about party rates

Additional Costs: None

Catering: Le Cafe Dodo, which is licensed

Just Imagine . . .

Just imagine what it would be like if the swallows didn't come with the Spring. No busy chittering from the telephone wires. No metallic crescents swooping into your garage. And no Autumn sky peppered with their wheeling display as they build up enough fuel to make that incredible journey back to Africa.

For thousands of years the Eastern population of the Bald Ibis **Geronticus eremita** migrated back and forth between the Red Sea and the Alps. Its arrival was cause for great celebration in many of the countries on its journey, a heritage which has been recorded in legend and on the earliest Egyptian hieroglyphics. Endowed with sacred significance in many religions through the millenia, it may even have been the first bird Noah released from the Ark, the ancient Hebrew name for bald ibis being identical to that of the raven.

In 1988 only 4 bald ibis arrived at the last traditional nesting site on the migration route, in the town of Birecik in Turkey.

There is one other population of bald ibis which have, so far as is known, developed independently from the eastern population. Under 150 birds still breed upon a cliff in the Massa National Park, Morocco. The Jersey Wildlife Preservation Trust maintains an expanding colony of these birds at the Jersey Zoo. The J.W.P.T., together with Wildlife Preservation Trust International has built breeding aviaries for bald ibis at Rabat, Morocco and is drawing up plans for a similar facility in Cairo. National zoo veterinarians from Cairo, Morocco and Algeria, all of whom have trained in Jersey, are part of a species survival plan with the aim to build up in the wild the world's last population of bald ibis. There is still a little hope for this extraordinary and unique avian character which has been so much a part of history and ecology across two hemispheres.

The bald ibis represents just one of the 60 species with whose survival the Wildlife Preservation Trusts are actively concerned.

For further information please write to the Trust Secretary, Jersey Wildlife Preservation Trust, Les Augrès Manor, Trinity, Jersey Channel Islands. Telephone (0534) 61949.

Facilities for Children: Children's meals are available. 'Gorilla Walk' play equipment

Facilities for the Disabled: Invalid chairs may be borrowed. There are toilets for the disabled and special parking reserved for disabled drivers. There are tarmac paths in some areas

Restrictions: No dogs, not even guide dogs. No feeding of the animals

This is the zoo which I consider the best in the world. The zoo itself (not just the animals) is a real delight. Very nearly all the species are endangered ones, and the breeding record is formidable. Tony Allchurch, the general administrator, in replying to my questions, called it Gerald Durrell's internationally renowned centre for breeding endangered species in captivity, and I cannot better that! There are animals here that you are unlikely to see elsewhere. The manor park and gardens are lovely. You can examine museum specimens on the touch tables, and have a go at brass rubbing. Finally, don't forget to say *Hullo* to Jambo, the most famous Lowland Gorilla in the world.

Curraghs Wildlife Park [93]

Ballaugh, Ramsey, Isle of Man
(Halfway between Ballaugh and Sulby on the A3)
Tel: 0624 897323
Proprietor: Isle of Man Government, Department of
Agriculture, Fisheries and Forestry

Open: During the Easter holidays, and from May to September inclusive from 10.00 to 6.00

Admission Fees: £1.20 adults, 60p children under 15 years, 60p OAPs. Party rates for groups of 25 and over: £1.00 adults, 50p children

Additional Costs: None

Catering: There is a lakeside cafeteria serving a basic range of cooked food, salads and snacks

Facilities for Children: There is a play area

Facilities for the Disabled: There is a suitable toilet. The site is level for wheelchairs

Restrictions: No dogs are allowed, nor is the feeding of animals. Vehicles of any sort are banned

In 1964 the Manx parliament acquired 211 acres (85 ha) of the Ballaugh Curraghs — an area of wetland — as a nature reserve. Later, 26 acres (10½ ha) were developed as a Wildlife Park, planned to blend into the natural surroundings. The basic idea is to show visitors the importance of the world's wetlands, which is not to say that all the animals have webbed feet. There is an Australian paddock, a monkey island and a South American lake, and much more. In 1988 a number of parrots and Père David's Deer were bred here. There is a nature trail, and for teachers a lecture room and educational leaflets are available.

Blair Drummond Safari and Leisure Park [94]

Blair Drummond, Stirling, Central Region, FK9 4UR
(Leave by Junction 10 from the M9 to the A84. The park is 5 miles
(8 km) from Stirling and 7 miles (11 km) from Callander)
Tel: 0786 841456
Proprietors: Richard Muir and Family

Open: Every day from one week before Easter until 1 October, between
10.00 and 5.30. Last admission is at 4.30

Admission Fees: £3.50 adults, £2.50 children between 3 and 15 years,
£2.50 OAPs. Party rates: £3.00 adults, £2.20 children, £2.50 OAPs. However,
to qualify for these prices the party must consist of at least 15 people and the
booking must have been made and paid for at least a week in advance. One
adult is admitted free with every 15 children

Additional Costs: Cinema 180 costs 50p

Catering: There is a self-service restaurant and a bar, and two ice cream
kiosks. Party menus and waitress service can be arranged if booked in
advance

Facilities for Children: Children's meals are available, and there are high
chairs. There is a pets farm, and various amusements

Facilities for the Disabled: Wheelchairs are available in the restaurant;
there are two toilets for the disabled. All the park is on one level

Restrictions: There are free kennels at the entrance for pets. There is a £1.00
returnable deposit for the padlock. No three-wheeler or soft-topped cars are
admitted, and visitors must not feed the animals

One can see a large range of mammals, either from one's car or from
the safari landrovers, or travel by boat to see the waterfowl and the
Chimpanzee Island. There are two young female African Elephants
here. There are also farm animals, and a pets corner as well as
performing sea lions. Leaflets are available to teachers, and several
species breed successfully, such as Chimpanzees, Père David's Deer,
camels, Llamas, American Bison, Sika Deer, Fallow Deer and Rhesus
Monkeys.

Edinburgh Butterfly and Insect World [95]

Melville Nurseries, Lasswade, Midlothian
(Between Edinburgh and Dalkeith on the A7)
Tel: 031 663 4932
Proprietor: Edinburgh Butterfly Farm Ltd

Open: Every day from the end of March to the end of October between 10.00 and 5.30

Admission Fees: £1.90 adults, £1.20 children, £1.20 OAPs. Party rate is £1.75. These prices are an estimate for 1989, so please ring to confirm

Additional Costs: None

Catering: There is a cafeteria

Facilities for Children: There is a children's playground

Facilities for the Disabled: Everything is accessible by wheelchair, and there is a toilet for the disabled

Restrictions: No dogs are allowed

As with all the butterfly gardens, this one consists of a large walk-through jungle full of butterflies, combined with a separate room housing numbers of other invertebrates such as spiders and scorpions. In addition, there is a breeding area open to visitors where you can watch caterpillars feeding on their specific foodplants. There is also a terrapin pond, and a bubbling mud spring, which is a feature I have not come across elsewhere. In the large pond one can see Koi Carp and Golden Orfe. Edinburgh specialises in breeding Heleconid butterflies and silkmoths. There is an education officer, and a suitable information pack is available on request. Visitors can also look round the garden centre.

HIMALAYAN BLACK BEARS ARRIVE AT GLASGOW ZOO

The grand opening of the Himalayan Black bear enclosure at Glasgow Zoo was planned to the last detail. It was the culmination of a very creative cooperation between Glasgow Zoo, Alloa Brewery and several animal welfare organisations. The final result provides "state of the art" facilities for the welfare and husbandry of the bears. Construction of this enormous enclosure had taken months, and the Zoo has every reason to be proud of it.

For the opening, a lavish tea party had been laid on. Our undoing was the rain. Never has there been such rain – torrents of water teaming down, giant raindrops bouncing off the ground. It rained and rained. Guests began to assemble in the marquee. The downpour was so strong that leaks threatened the elegantly laid tables groaning with dainties. Just before Johnny Morris – our guest of honour – arrived, water collecting on its roof caused the marquee to collapse. Total disaster was avoided only by plucky waitresses throwing themselves at the tent poles to keep them upright while others rushed into the wet to re-secure the guy ropes.

Johnny Morris was escorted into the marquee amidst a flock of umbrellas. The public address system, perhaps overawed by the occasion and the climate, decided to pass out. Johnny gave an entertaining speech nonetheless, against the roar of rain hitting canvas. Then, he went into the storm to unveil a plaque and inspect the bears and their enclosure. It certainly must be one of the best Black bear enclosures in Europe. Snug and dry in their dens, the bears showed remarkable complaisance in the circumstances. After all, this was really their day.

Glasgow Zoo Calderpark Uddingston Glasgow G71 7RZ
Telephone: 041-771 1185

Glasgow Zoo [96]

Calderpark, Uddingston, Glasgow, G71 7RZ
(On the A74, just west of the M73/M74 junction)
Tel: 041 771 1185
Proprietor: The Zoological Society of Glasgow
and West of Scotland

Open: Every day except Christmas Day between 10.00 and 5–6.00

Admission Fees: £2.50 adults, £1.40 children, £1.40 OAPs and the unemployed on production of their UB40 card. Party rate for groups of 12 or over, £1.50 adults, 80p children (for 1988)

Additional Costs: Children's amusements

Catering: There is a cafeteria, and kiosks selling food

Facilities for Children: None stated

Facilities for the Disabled: There are ramps where necessary, and toilets for the disabled

Restrictions: No dogs are allowed. Visitors are not allowed to feed the animals, and unaccompanied children are not admitted

Over recent years, zoos have been changing and improving beyond all recognition. At Glasgow there is now a marvellous tiger enclosure and more suitable accommodation for the Himalayan Black Bears. The collection itself includes a number of species of reptiles including uncommonly seen Gila Monsters. There are not too many birds, those there are being waterfowl, parrots and fowl of various sorts, and Emus and rheas. There is a tropical fish collection, and Honey Bees, a whole heap of assorted ungulates and a good collection of cats. This was the first British zoo to breed Geoffroy's Cat, and they also breed leopards, porcupines and other animals. There is a good education department. The new bear enclosure that I mentioned above, is a large, wooded valley.

The Wildfowl Trust [97]

Caerlaverock, Eastpark Farm, Caerlaverock, Dumfriesshire, DG1 4RS
(Follow the Solway Coast Heritage Trail signs from Annan, or the Trust signs from Dumfries)
Tel: 038777 200
Proprietor: The Wildfowl Trust

Open: Every day from 16 September to 30 April except for Christmas Eve and Christmas Day, from 9.30 to 5.00

Admission Fees: £1.70 adults, 90p children between the ages of 4 and 16 years, £1.30 OAPs. Party rates for groups of 20 or more £1.20. Enquire about special rates for school parties

Additional Costs: None

Catering: None

Facilities for Children: There are no special facilities, but children are welcome, especially in school parties

Facilities for the Disabled: There are viewing facilities in the new Tower Hide

Restrictions: No dogs are allowed in the reserve

This refuge is adjacent to the National Nature Reserve on the Solway Firth, and not far from Caerlaverock Castle. Here, on a site of 1400 acres (567 ha) you can see huge flocks of Barnacle Geese as this is the main wintering ground of the entire Spitzbergen population — around 10,400 birds. You can also watch Pink Footed and Greylag Geese, Whooper and Bewick's Swans and at least nine species of ducks as well as thousands of Oystercatchers, Golden Plovers and other waders. Birds of prey like Peregrines, Merlins, Hen Harriers and Short Eared Owls may also be seen. The number of places where you can see such huge numbers of birds are not many these days, but do note that the reserve is open only in the winter, which is handy as a lot of other places close down at this time of the year.

Anglesey Sea Zoo [98]

The Oyster Hatchery, Brynsiencyn, Anglesey, Gwynedd, LL61 6TQ
(2 miles (3 km) from Brynsiencyn village on the shore of the Menai Strait)
Tel: 0248 71411
Proprietor: Anglesey Sea Zoo

Open: Every day from early February to early November from 10.00 to 5.00, though during July and August the times are 9.30 to 5.30

Admission Fees: (for 1988 — they will have increased by 1989) £1.95 adults, 95p children under 18 years, £1.50 OAPs. Party rates (for groups of more than 12): £1.60 adults, 80p children, £1.20 OAPs

Additional Costs: None

Catering: There is a restaurant, ice cream stalls and picnic tables

Facilities for Children: There is a children's menu, a nappy-changing facility, and rides for children

Facilities for the Disabled: There are ramps where appropriate and a toilet for the disabled

Restrictions: Dogs are allowed if they are kept on leads

This collection of marine life is the largest aquarium in Wales. If that doesn't sound too interesting, go to the place and surprise yourself. There are, of course, tanks full of fish, but instead of being yet another boring old display, they are set out to a theme, such as a harbour wall, a shoaling spectacular, and so on. There are displays of lobsters, crabs and oysters and there is even a tank where you can touch the animals. It really is impressive, and the guide book is not only packed with great pictures and useful information, it even tells you how to set up your own tanks. At this Sea Zoo they breed and grow on lobsters for release into coastal waters. Guided tours are available at extra cost, and questionnaires can be obtained by teachers, aimed at different age groups, and when you tire of looking at animals there are all sorts of other things to do, all with a watery theme. There is for example a model boat tank, an aquablaster water game, a boat in a sandpit, and finally there is a seafood shop. Anglesey Sea Zoo is a must for anyone in the area.

Butterfly Palace [99]

Ffordd Penmynydd, Menai Bridge, Isle of Anglesey, Gwynedd, LL59 5RP
(On the B5420, a short distance north west of the Menai Bridge)
Tel: 0248 712474
Proprietors: Mr and Mrs H.J. Hughes

Open: Every day throughout the season until the end of October between 10.00 and 5.30

Admission Fees: No information available

Additional Costs: No information

Catering: There is a cafe selling home made refreshments, Welsh teas and ice cream

Facilities for Children: There is a pets corner

Facilities for the Disabled: None stated, but they do say that disabled persons are welcome

Restrictions: No information

This collection is a typically interesting walk through jungle full of free-flying exotic butterflies. There is also a section on species that breed in Wales, which is a good idea, and a butterfly garden planted with species of plants that attract butterflies. Visitors can also see a variety of other invertebrates such as spiders, locusts, giant stick insects, and ants. One might notice terrapins basking around the edges of the pond inside the jungle. For teachers there is an education centre, complete with a video presentation.

Fairbourne and Barmouth Steam Railway and Butterfly Safari [100]

Beach Road, Fairbourne, Gwynedd, LL38 2PZ
(9 miles (14½ km) south of Dolgellau and 11 miles (18 km)
north of Tywyn, just off the B493)
Tel: 0341 250084 for recorded information, otherwise
0341 250362 or 0341 250083
Proprietor: North Wales Narrow Gauge Railway Ltd

Open: From Easter week to the end of October between 10.00 and 5.30

Admission Fees: £1.80 adults, £1.00 children under 16 years, £1.40 OAPs. Party rates for groups of 12 or over £1.50, and children in such groups receive a spotter pack. These prices are for the Butterfly Safari only

Additional Costs: Train rides: 2nd class return £2.30 adult, £1.35 children, £1.75 OAPs

Catering: There is a restaurant at the far end of the railway line

Facilities for Children: At the far end of the line there is a Mother and Baby room for nursing mothers

Facilities for the Disabled: The railway has facilities for carrying two wheelchairs

Restrictions: No dogs are allowed in the Butterfly Safari

This butterfly collection and like others contains a walk-through jungle where you can wander about amidst tropical plants and watch free-flying butterflies all around you. Where it differs from many others is that there is also a small mammals section which houses Leopard Cats, Ring Tailed Lemurs and Racoons, which breed here. Incidentally, at one time the only butterflies one ever saw, apart from native species in the garden, were in glass cases. Butterfly gardens in the west have now become such big business that breeding farms to supply them with captive bred stock can be found in the tropics, thus bringing employment, and reducing the drain on wild stocks.

Welsh Hawking Centre [101]

Weycock Road, Barry, South Glamorgan, CF6 9AA
(Halfway down the B4050)
Tel: 0446 734687
Proprietor: C.J. Griffiths

Open: Every day except Christmas Day from 10.30 to 5.00

Admission Fees: £2.00 adults, £1.00 children under 14 years, £1.00 OAPs. Party rates are 10% less than these figures

Additional Costs: None

Catering: There is a cafeteria and an ice cream stall

Facilities for Children: There is an adventure playground

Facilities for the Disabled: There are ramps where they are needed

Restrictions: None

This is a centre where birds of prey are bred. Visitors can enjoy watching these magnificent and endlessly fascinating birds at remarkably close quarters. There are also demonstrations of the ancient skill of falconry when birds are flown to artificial lures.

Dublin Zoo [102]

Phoenix Park, Dublin 8
(In the northeast corner of Phoenix Park)
Tel: 0001 771425
Proprietor: The Royal Zoological Society of Ireland

Open: Every day from 9.30 to 6.00 in summer and till 4.00 in winter, except on Sundays when it opens at 11.00

Admission Fees: £3.20 adults, £1.60 children between 3 and 14 years, OAPs and handicapped visitors are admitted free. Family tickets which admit two adults and four children cost £10.00. Party rates (for groups of twenty or over) £2.60 adults, £1.30 children, and one adult is admitted free with every ten children

Additional Costs: Train rides are 25p, and admission to pets corner is 25p

Catering: There are cafeterias, restaurants, ice cream stalls and shops, all of which sell food

Facilities for Children: Children's meals are available

Facilities for the Disabled: Two wheelchairs are available

Restrictions: No pets are allowed

Dublin Zoo has long had a reputation in the zoo world. It is situated in one of Europe's largest public parks and encompasses 30 acres (12 ha) of attractive gardens. Within the collection of animals are some of the rarest. They currently have a display of Koalas, which they are hoping to continue permanently. Notable breeding successes include Snow Leopards, Persian Leopards, Lion Tailed Macaques, tapirs and Giraffes. Educational facilities are available, and during the winter there are a variety of events, including a visit by Santa Claus at Christmas, and I cannot think of a nicer place to first come face to face with this traditional figure than in a good zoo.

Fota Wildlife Park [103]

Carrigtwohill, County Cork
(10 miles (16 km) east of Cork city on the road to Cobh)
Tel: 021 812678
Proprietor: Fota Wildlife Park is a company with charitable
status

Open: Every day from the beginning of April to the end of October from
10.00 to 6.00 on weekdays and 11.00 to 6.00 on Sundays.

Admission Fees: £2.20 adults, £1.10 children under 14 years, £1.70
students, £1.10 OAPs and disabled visitors. Party rates: £1.90 adults, 95p
children, OAPs and disabled visitors, £1.50 students. These are all prices for
1989

Additional Costs: Car parking, which also includes entry into the world
famous arboretum, is £1.50 per car

Catering: There is a lakeside coffee shop and picnic areas

Facilities for Children: There is a childrens corner and playground

Facilities for the Disabled: There are ramps where necessary, and toilets
suitable for disabled visitors, and wheelchairs are available

Restrictions: No pets are allowed, nor is the feeding of any of the animals

Fota Wildlife Park is part of the Royal Zoological Society of Ireland. The
collection is strong on ungulates, of which there are many species,

Fota Wildlife Pa

At Fota Wildlife Park, visitors can view over 70 species of wildlife in natural,
open surroundings with no obvious barriers. Giraffes, zebras and antelope
enjoy 40 acres of grassland, through which visitors walk on an unfenced roa
Monkeys swing through trees on lake islands. Wallabies, lemurs and macav
wander freely throughout the Park. Only the cheetahs are enclosed!

Amenities include Tour Train, Children's Corner and Coffee Shop.

10 miles from Cork city. Turn for Cobh from Rt. N.25 (Cork – Rosslare/Wexford Roa

FOTA WILDLIFE PARK, CARRIGTWOHILL, CO. CORK. Tel (021) 812678/8127

including a herd of the beautiful Scimitar Horned Oryx. There are also large numbers of primates, and some macaws and other birds like penguins, ratities and flamingoes. There is also a waterfowl collection. The breeding group of Lion Tailed Macaques is one of only three in the British Isles, and one can see one of the largest Cheetah breeding areas in the world — the only breeding group of these animals in Ireland. The animals have large enclosures and the monkeys are either on islands or roaming free. Educational leaflets are available on request.

The Collections Listed Alphabetically

Abbotsbury Swannery, Dorset
Anglesey Sea Zoo, Anglesey
Animal Gardens (The), Lincolnshire
Appleby Castle Conservation Centre,
  Cumbria
Banham Zoo and Monkey Sanctuary,
  Norfolk
Bentley Wildfowl Trust and Motor
  Museum, East Sussex
Birdland and Windrush Trout Farm,
  Gloucestershire
Birdworld, Surrey
Birmingham Nature Centre,
  Warwickshire
Blair Drummond Safari and Leisure
  Park, Scotland
Blean Bird Park, Kent
Bolton Aquarium, Lancashire
Brambles English Wildlife Park, Kent
Bridgemere Wildlife Park, Cheshire
Brighton Aquarium and Dolphinarium,
  Sussex
Bristol Zoo, Avon
Buckfast Butterfly Farm, Devon
Busbridge Lakes Ornamental
  Waterfowl, Surrey
Butterfly Centre (The), East Sussex
Butterfly Centre (The), Kent
Butterfly Palace, Anglesey
Cannon Aquarium and Vivarium,
  Greater Manchester
Chessington World of Adventures,
  Surrey
Chester Zoo, Cheshire
Child Beale Wildlife Trust, Berkshire
Colchester Zoological Gardens, Essex
Cotswold Wildlife Park, Oxfordshire

Cricket St Thomas Wildlife Park,
  Somerset
Curraghs Wildlife Park, Isle of Man
Deen City Farm, Surrey
Domestic Fowl Trust, Worcestershire
Drayton Manor Park, Staffordshire
Drusilla's Park, East Sussex
Dublin Zoo, Republic of Ireland
Easton Farm Park, Suffolk
Edinburgh Butterfly and Insect World,
  Scotland
Exmoor Bird Gardens, Devon
Fairbourne and Barmouth Steam
  Railway and Butterfly Farm, Wales
Falconry Centre (The),
  Gloucestershire
Ferne Animal Sanctuary, Somerset
Fota Wildlife Park, Rep. of Ireland
Gatwick Zoo and Gatwick Butterfly
  and Tropical Gardens, Surrey
Glasgow Zoo, Scotland
Great Shire Horse Centre (The),
  Dorset
Guisborough Grange Wildlife Park,
  Northamptonshire
Haigh Miniature Zoo, Lancashire
Hawk Conservancy (The), Hampshire
Heeley City Farm, Yorkshire
Howletts Zoo Park, Kent
Jersey Wildlife Preservation Trust,
  Channel Islands
Kentish Town City Farm, London
Kilverstone Wildlife Park and
  Miniature Horse Stud, Norfolk
Leeds Castle, Kent
Linton Zoological Gardens,
  Cambridgeshire

Lions of Longleat Safari Park,
Wiltshire
Living World, East Sussex
London Butterfly House, Middlesex
Long Sutton Butterfly Farm,
Lincolnshire
Lyme Regis Marine Aquarium, Dorset
Marwell Zoological Park, Hampshire
Mole Hall Wildlife Park, Essex
New Forest Butterfly Farm (The),
Hampshire
Newquay Zoo, Cornwall
Norton Tropical Bird Gardens, Suffolk
Otter Trust (The), Suffolk
Padstow Tropical Bird Gardens,
Cornwall
Paignton Aquarium, Devon
Paradise Park, Cornwall
Paultons Park, Hampshire
Port Lympne Zoo Park, Mansion and
Gardens, Kent
Riber Castle Wildlife Park, Derbyshire
St Werburghs City Farm, Bristol,
Avon
Sewerby Park Zoo, East Yorkshire
Shaldon Wildlife Trust, Devon
Shropshire Country World,
Shropshire
Skegness Natureland, Marine Zoo and
Seal Sanctuary, Lincolnshire
Stagsden Bird Gardens, Bedfordshire
Stratford Upon Avon Butterfly Farm
and Jungle Safari, Warwickshire
Thrigby Hall Wildlife Gardens, Norfolk

Tropical Bird Gardens (The),
Somerset
Tropical Butterflies (Barrow) Ltd,
Suffolk
Tropical Butterfly Garden (The),
South Humberside
Twycross Zoo, Warwickshire
Underwater World, Surrey
Waddesdon Manor, Buckinghamshire
Wellgate Community Farm, Essex
Welsh Hawking Centre, South
Glamorgan
West Midland Safari and Leisure
Park, Worcestershire
Wildfowl Trust (The), Cambridgeshire
Wildfowl Trust (The), Dumfriesshire
Wildfowl Trust (The), Gloucestershire
Wildfowl Trust (The), Lancashire
Wildfowl Trust (The), Sussex
Wildfowl Trust (The), Tyne and Wear
Willersmill Fish Farm and Wild Animal
Sanctuary, Hertfordshire
Windmill Hill City Farm, Avon
Windsor Safari Park, Berkshire
Wingham Bird Park, Kent
Woburn Wild Animal Kingdom,
Bedfordshire
Worldwide Butterflies and
Lullingstone Silk Farm, Dorset
Zoological Society of London,
Whipsnade Zoo, Bedfordshire
Zoological Trust of Guernsey,
Channel Islands

The Collection Listed by Animal Groups

Mammals

Animal Gardens (The), Lincolnshire
Appleby Castle Conservation Centre,
    Cumbria
Banham Zoo and Monkey Sanctuary,
    Norfolk
Birmingham Nature Centre,
    Warwickshire
Blair Drummond Safari and Leisure
    Park, Scotland
Brambles English Wildlife Park, Kent
Bridgemere Wildlife Park, Cheshire
Bristol Zoo, Avon
Chessington World of Adventures,
    Surrey
Chester Zoo, Cheshire
Colchester Zoo, Essex
Cotswold Wildlife Park, Oxfordshire
Cricket St Thomas Wildlife Park,
    Somerset
Curraghs Wildlife Park, Isle of Man
Deen City Farm, Surrey
Drayton Manor Park, Staffordshire
Drusilla's Park, East Sussex
Dublin Zoo, Republic of Ireland
Easton Farm Park, Suffolk
Ferne Animal Sanctuary, Somerset
Fota Wildlife Park, Republic of Ireland
Gatwick Zoo and Gatwick Butterfly
    and Tropical Gardens, Surrey
Great Shire Horse Centre (The),
    Dorset
Guisborough Grange Wildlife Park,
    Northamptonshire
Haigh Miniature Zoo, Dorset
Heeley City Farm, Yorkshire

Howletts Zoo Park, Kent
Jersey Wildlife Preservation Trust,
    Channel Islands
Kentish Town City Farm, London
Kilverstone Wildlife Park and
    Miniature Horse Stud, Norfolk
Linton Zoo, Cambridgeshire
Lions of Longleat (The), Wiltshire
Marwell Zoological Park,
    Hampshire
Mole Hall Wildlife Park, Essex
Newquay Zoo, Cornwall
Otter Trust (The), Suffolk
Port Lympne Zoo Park, Mansion and
    Gardens, Kent
Riber Castle, Derbyshire
St Werburghs City Farm, Bristol,
    Avon
Sewerby Park Zoo, East Yorkshire
Shaldon Wildlife Trust, Devon
Shropshire Country World,
    Shropshire
Skegness Natureland, Marine Zoo and
    Seal Sanctuary, Lincolnshire
Thrigby Hall Wildlife Gardens, Norfolk
Twycross Zoo, Warwickshire
Wellgate Community Farm, Essex
West Midlands Safari Park,
    Worcestershire
Willersmill Fish Farm and Wild Animal
    Sanctuary, Hertfordshire
Windmill Hill City Farm, Avon
Windsor Safari Park, Berkshire
Woburn Wild Animal Kingdom,
    Bedfordshire
Zoological Society of London,
    Whipsnade Zoo, Bedfordshire

THE COLLECTIONS LIST

Birds

Abbotsbury Swannery, Dorset
Animal Gardens (The), Lincolnshire
Appleby Castle Conservation Centre, Cumbria
Bentley Wildfowl Trust and Motor Museum, East Sussex
Birdland, Gloucestershire
Birdworld, Surrey
Birmingham Nature Centre, Warwickshire
Blean Bird Park, Kent
Brambles English Wildlife Park, Kent
Bridgemere Wildlife Park, Cheshire
Bristol Zoo, Avon
Busbridge Lakes Ornamental Waterfowl, Surrey
Chessington World of Adventures, Surrey
Chester Zoo, Cheshire
Child-Beale Wildlife Trust, Berkshire
Colchester Zoo, Essex
Cotswold Wildlife Park, Oxfordshire
Cricket St Thomas Wildlife Park, Somerset
Curraghs Wildlife Park, Isle of Man
Domestic Fowl Trust, Worcestershire
Drayton Manor Park, Staffordshire
Drusilla's Park, East Sussex
Dublin Zoo, Republic of Ireland
Exmoor Bird Gardens, Devon
Falconry Centre (The), Gloucestershire
Fota Wildlife Park, Republic of Ireland
Gatwick Zoo and Gatwick Butterfly and Tropical Gardens, Surrey
Guisborough Grange Wildlife Park, Northamptonshire
Haigh Miniature Zoo, Dorset
Hawk Conservancy (The), Hampshire
Howlettes Zoo Park, Kent
Jersey Wildlife Preservation Trust, Channel Islands

Kilverstone Wildlife Park and Miniature Horse Stud, Norfolk
Leeds Castle, Kent
Linton Zoo, Cambridgeshire
Marwell Zoological Park, Hampshire
Mole Hall Wildlife Park, Essex
Newquay Zoo, Cornwall
Norton Tropical Bird Gardens, Suffolk
Padstow Tropical Bird Gardens, Cornwall
Paradise Park, Cornwall
Paultons Park, Hampshire
Port Lympne Zoo Park, Mansion and Gardens, Kent
Sewerby Park Zoo, East Yorkshire
Shaldon Wildlife Trust, Devon
Skegness Natureland, Marine Zoo and Seal Sanctuary, Lincolnshire
Stagsden Bird Gardens, Bedfordshire
Tropical Bird Gardens, Somerset
Twycross Zoo, Warwickshire
Waddesdon Manor, Buckinghamshire
Wildfowl Trust (The), Cambridgeshire
Wildfowl Trust (The), Dumfriesshire
Wildfowl Trust (The), Gloucestershire
Wildfowl Trust (The), Lancashire
Wildfowl Trust (The), Sussex
Wildfowl Trust (The), Tyne and Wear
Willersmill Fish Farm and Wild Animal Sanctuary, Hertfordshire
Windsor Safari Park, Bedfordshire
Wingham Bird Park, Kent
Woburn Wild Animal Kingdom, Bedfordshire
Zoological Society of London, Whipsnade Zoo, Bedfordshire

Reptiles

Bristol Zoo, Avon
Cannon Aquarium and Vivarium, Greater Manchester

155

Chester Zoo, Cheshire
Drayton Manor Park, Staffordshire
Jersey Wildlife Preservation Trust,
  Channel Islands
Newquay Zoo, Cornwall
Thrigby Hall Wildlife Gardens, Norfolk
Tropical Butterfly Garden (The),
  South Humberside
Twycross Zoo, Warwickshire

Fish

Anglesey Sea Zoo, Anglesey
Bolton Aquarium, Lancashire
Brighton Aquarium and Dolphinarium,
  East Sussex
Cannon Aquarium and Vivarium,
  Greater Manchester
Living World, East Sussex
Lyme Regis Marine Aquarium, Dorset
Paignton Aquarium, Devon
Underwater World, Surrey
Willersmill Fish Farm and Wild Animal
  Sanctuary, Hertfordshire

Invertebrates

Buckfast Butterfly Farm, Devon
Butterfly Centre (The), Kent
Butterfly Centre (The), East Sussex
Fairbourne and Barmouth Steam
  Railway and Butterfly Farm,
  Gwynedd
Gatwick Zoo and Gatwick Butterfly
  and Tropical Gardens, Surrey
Lions of Longleat Safari Park,
  Wiltshire
Living World, East Sussex
London Butterfly House, Middlesex
Mole Hall Wildlife Park, Essex
New Forest Butterfly Farm (The),
  Hampshire
Padstow Tropical Bird Gardens,
  Cornwall
Shropshire Country World,
  Shropshire
Stratford Upon Avon Butterfly Farm
  and Jungle Safari, Warwickshire
Tropical Butterflies (Barrow), Suffolk
Tropical Butterfly Garden (The),
  South Humberside
Worldwide Butterflies and
  Lullingstone Silk Farm, Dorset